6 AUG 81

RATE YOUR OWN
CHESS
REVISED EDITION

RATE YOUR OWN
CHESS

REVISED EDITION

RAISE YOUR CHESS IQ IN
MATE-RATER COMPETITION

INCLUDES COMPUTER CHESS NOTATION

F. DONALD BLOSS

 VAN NOSTRAND REINHOLD COMPANY
NEW YORK CINCINNATI TORONTO LONDON MELBOURNE

To the Lands of Eminence
and to Helen and Larry

First published in paperback in 1981
Copyright © 1972, 1981 by Van Nostrand Reinhold Company
Library of Congress Catalog Card Number 72-2355
ISBN 0-442-21261-5

Printed in the United States of America

Van Nostrand Reinhold Company
135 West 50th Street, New York, NY 10020

Van Nostrand Reinhold Ltd.
1410 Birchmount Road, Scarborough, Ontario M1P 2E7

Van Nostrand Reinhold Australia Pty. Ltd.
17 Queen Street, Mitcham, Victoria 3132

Van Nostrand Reinhold Company Ltd.
Molly Millars Lane, Wokingham, Berkshire, England RG11 2PY

Cloth edition published 1972 by Van Nostrand Reinhold Company

16   15   14   13   12   11   10   9   8   7   6   5   4   3   2   1

Contents

Acknowledgments

I am grateful to the following rated chessplayers for taking the tests which made the mate-raters possible: William Aulson, Robert Austin, William Bochman, George F. Cake, John Cardinale, Carl Diesen, Mark Diesen, Andrew Downey, Jr., Peter Duncan, David Glaser, Carlos Gorostiaga, Arthur Heigl, Skip Hoffman, John F. Hurt, Dr. Ralph Jollensten, Harry Judy, David Karch, Major Robert Karch, Carl Kiser, Gregory Krimer, Rick Kuhn, Anthony Laster, Capt. George Martin, John Mingos, James Monacell, Leonard C. Morgan, Hans Multhopp, Edmund Nash, K. Davis O'Kelley, Paul Oldaker, M. R. Owen, Dr. Sidney Phillips, Warren Porter, Robert Riley, III, Howard E. Ross, Stephen Ruddel, Harvey Starr, David Terry, David Vecellio, Dane Victorine, Joseph Viggiano and John H. Wilson.

It is a special pleasure to thank Leonard Morgan of the Roanoke Chess Club for his help at all stages of this project. For their help in locating additional chessplayers to take the tests, I am also indebted to Jim Glanville, to Robert Karch, and to Howard Evans Ross.

Dr. John Louisnathan kindly wrote one of the necessary computer programs, and Martin Eiss provided the attractive line drawings. I would also like to thank Daniel Sandhaus.

My daughter, Mrs. Robert Kensler, performed most of the computations (with an assist by James F. Light).

Introduction

The chess problems in *Rate Your Own Chess* are intended to sharpen the ability of intermediate players to recognize winning moves as well as to permit each reader to determine his approximate United States Chess Federation rating, and thus his approximate strength as a player. The ratings are determined from the time required by the reader for solution of each of fourteen special problems called mate-raters.

Players who lack either the occasion or the inclination to obtain a USCF rating by competing publicly against rated players in tournaments may welcome the mate-raters as an opportunity to determine their standings in private. Of course a player may perform above or below his usual capacity on any single mate-rater problem, and a true USCF rating more likely reflects a player's average performance over an extensive number of games. Thus a player's average performance on all fourteen mate-raters should better approximate his true USCF rating than his performance on any single one.

Each problem has been illustrated as set up on a real chessboard. This favors the beginning player who may be unduly handicapped if chess problems are presented in the two-dimensional format traditional to most chess books. Moreover, these realistic representations take the reader one step closer to the above-the-board experience so necessary to proficiency in chess.

The problems are divided into one-move-to-mate problems, two-move-to-mate problems, and three-move-to-mate problems, so that difficulty, as a rule, gradually increases as the player works through the book. The one-move-to-mate problems are all ordinary problems intended solely for practice. In the other sections there are ordinary problems, warm-up problems and mate-rater problems. For most players the practice and warm-up problems will be somewhat easier than the mate-rater that follows them.

For each problem, the correct answer (and often a discussion) is given on the page immediately following. In specifying moves, squares will usually be fully designated — for example, KB3 rather than the more brief B3 — even though no ambiguity would arise if the briefer designation were used. This may make it easier for relatively inexperienced players to follow the solutions. For a mate-rater problem, the reader should record his solution — as well as the time it took to reach the solution and record his answer — in the blanks provided or on a separate sheet of paper.

The basic tenet of the mate-rater problems is that a more highly rated player will perceive a winning move more quickly than a lower-rated player. Both the warm-up problems and the mate-raters presented here were actually tested on a group of players with current USCF ratings (for details of this survey see the Appendix.) The mate-rater problems were chosen as good tests because they were the problems that showed the highest correlation between a player's rating and his time for solving the problem — the players with the highest rating took the shortest time. For some of the relatively easy problems, which have been included among the warm-ups, the players with low ratings frequently reported shorter times than those with high ratings. Quite possibly the higher-rated players, suspecting a subtle trap, checked and rechecked their solutions, whereas the lower-rated players plunged blithely ahead, avoiding grief only because the problem *was* easy.

In most cases the players found the one-move problems easier than the two-move problems, and the three-move problems the most difficult (time-consuming) to solve. However, some of the later two-move problems were more difficult than many of the three-move problems. As a rule, the less experienced players found the three-move mate raters difficult to solve in 10 minutes, even though many of these same mate-raters were immediately obvious to the more highly practiced, higher-rated players.

On the pages following each mate-rater problem there is, along with the solution, a table that will convert the time it took to solve the problem into an approximate USCF rating. Three ratings are given: an approximate rating, a high estimate of rating, and a low estimate of rating. The high and low values define the range in which the rating is likely to fall, since naturally the approximate rating can only be pinpointed within a certain margin of error. If a reader times himself on all fourteen of the mate-raters, the average of his fourteen approximate ratings will usually be within 100 or 200 points of his true USCF rating.

1. Chessboard Notation

The basic moves and strategies of chess are probably familiar to most readers of this book. However, for the convenience of players with little experience in recording chess moves, the two main methods for recording moves, namely, the *descriptive notation* and the *algebraic notation,* will be described. The descriptive notation has prevailed in English- and Spanish-speaking countries, whereas the algebraic notation, after its introduction into Europe in the 18th century, was widely adopted by German-speaking countries and from them spread throughout the world. Currently, even in English-speaking countries, the algebraic notation is gaining adherents. Its major advantages are its simplicity and, as is becoming increasingly apparent, its easy adaptation for use with chess-playing computers or microcomputers.

Descriptive Notation

The symbols commonly used by United States players are as follows:

QR	=	Queen's Rook
QN	=	Queen's Knight
QB	=	Queen's Bishop
Q	=	Queen
K	=	King
KB	=	King's Bishop
KN	=	King's Knight
KR	=	King's Rook
P	=	Pawn
en prise	=	subject to immediate capture
0–0	=	castles King-side
0–0–0	=	castles Queen-side
x	=	captures
–	=	Moves to
ch (or +)	=	check
dis ch	=	discovered check
dbl ch (or ++)	=	double check
e.p.	=	*en passant*
!	=	good move
?	=	bad move

The chessboard is divided into eight files (Fig. 1), each named after the piece that occupied this file at the start of the game. Similarly, the board is divided into eight ranks that run perpendicular to the files (Fig. 2). These ranks are numbered from 1 to 8, a player's first rank being closest to him, his eighth rank farthest away. Consequently a single rank has two designations, one from WHITE's standpoint, another from BLACK's (See Fig. 2). Moreover, these two alternate rank designations always total 9, this being the so-called "rule of nines." Thus, rank 1 for WHITE coincides with rank 8 for BLACK, etc. Any single square on the chessboard may be located by specifying its file and rank. But each square may be designated from either WHITE's viewpoint as well as from BLACK's (Fig. 3). For example, the square indicated by an arrow in Figure 3 can be called QB8 (from WHITE's viewpoint) or **QB1** (from BLACK's).

For the descriptive notation this book will utilize **bold-faced type** to designate black chessmen and to specify squares from BLACK's viewpoint. Thus, N indicates a White Knight; **N** indicates a Black Knight. Similarly, QB1 and **QB8** designate the same square from WHITE's and BLACK's viewpoint, respectively.

To record a move, first write the symbol of the man moved, then write a hyphen, which means "moves to", and last write the symbol of the square moved to. Thus, N-KB3 indicates that a White Knight moved to square KB3. Similarly **N-KB6** indicates a Black Knight moved to this same square. If two White Knights were in position to move onto square KB3, the square of departure would be indicated in parentheses to specify the particular Knight moved. Thus N(K5)-KB3 stipulates that the White Knight on square K5 was moved to square KB3.

If on his 14th move of the game, WHITE used his bishop to capture BLACK's Rook, this is written

14.B x **R**

If on *his* 14th move BLACK used his Queen to capture WHITE's Queen, this is written

14. . . .   **Q** x **Q**

The three dots indicate that the description of WHITE's 14th move has been omitted. The 14th moves by both would be simultaneously recorded as

14.B x **R**   **Q** x **Q**

As shown in the examples above, BLACK's move is always given second. Suppose that on his 14th move, WHITE had *two* Knights in position to capture a Black Rook; in such a case the square of departure for the Knight actually moved would be indicated in parentheses. Thus

14. N(KB6) x R

indicates that the White Knight on square KB6 captures the Black Rook.

A Pawn that reaches the eighth rank must be promoted to a Queen, Rook, Bishop, or Knight. In chess notation the piece to which a Pawn is promoted is usually enclosed in parentheses. For example, P-B8(Q) indicates that a White Pawn was advanced to square B8 and promoted to a Queen. Similarly, P-B8(N) indicates it was promoted to a Knight. When a Pawn is promoted to a piece less valuable than a Queen, it is said to be *underpromoted*. Sometimes underpromotion is necessary to avoid stalemating an opponent who is already badly beaten. On rare occasions underpromotion to a Knight may effect an immediate checkmate of the opposition. This is possible because a Knight is the only chess piece whose move cannot be duplicated by the Queen.

Algebraic Notation

In the algebraic notation, which the World Chess Federation endorses, the eight files (Fig. 1) are designated, from left to right, by the lowercase letters *a* through *h*. The ranks (Fig. 2) are numbered from 1 to 8, according to their distance from WHITE, regardless of whether WHITE or BLACK is making the move. Each square can now be denoted by specifying the letter of its file and the number of its rank. Thus, d4 specifies a particular square (Fig. 3). Moves are described by using a capital letter (B, R, N, K, or Q) to designate the piece being moved plus the symbols for the squares of *departure* and *arrival*, with the symbols for these squares separated by a hyphen. Thus, Ng1-f3 indicates the move of a Knight from square g1 to f3. For Pawn moves, the symbol for the chessman is omitted. Hence, d2–d4 denotes movement of a Pawn from square d2 to d4. For any move involving capture of an enemy chessman, as for the descriptive notation, an x is substituted for the hyphen. For example, Ng1xf3 would indicate that the Knight captured the enemy chessman on square f3. The symbols +, ++, 0–0, 0–0–0, and e.p. have the same significance as in the descriptive notation.

During a game, when opposing players record their moves, they use an abbreviated form of the algebraic notation. In it the symbol for the square of departure is omitted (unless ambiguity results from such omission). Thus, d4 denotes the Pawn move d2–d4. Similarly, Nf3 would indicate the Knight move Ng1-f3, whereas Nxf3 would indicate the move Ng1xf3. However, if two knights are each in position to move to f3, for example, one on g1 and the other on h4, the move would be described as Ngf3 or Nhf3, depending upon which knight was moved. On the other hand, if the two knights had been located on the same file, for example, on squares g1 and g5, the move to f3 would be specified as N1f3 or N5f3, depending upon which knight was moved.

Microcomputers use the algebraic notation for moves but generally omit the symbol for the chess piece. Thus, they usually display only the algebraic symbols for the squares of departure and arrival. Hence, the Knight move specified algebraically as Nf3-e5 would be displayed as f3-e5. Some microcomputers use capital letters to designate one or more of the files *a* to *h*. In such case the Knight move might be displayed as F3-E5.

Notations Used in this Book

Moves will be specified (1) by descriptive notation in the body of the text and also (2) by nonabbreviated algebraic notation to the right of the text or below it. The symbol likely to be displayed by a microcomputer for each move can then be easily generated by omitting, from the nonabbreviated algebraic notation for the move, all but the symbols for the squares of departure and arrival.

Fig. 1. In the descriptive notation the chessboard is organized into eight files that are called: (*l. to r.*) the Queen's Rook file (QR), the Queen's Knight file (QN), the Queen's Bishop file (QB), the Queen's file (Q), the King's file (K), the King's Bishop file (KB), the King's Knight file (KN), and the King's Rook file (KR). In the algebraic notation the files (*l. to r.*) are designated *a* to *h*.

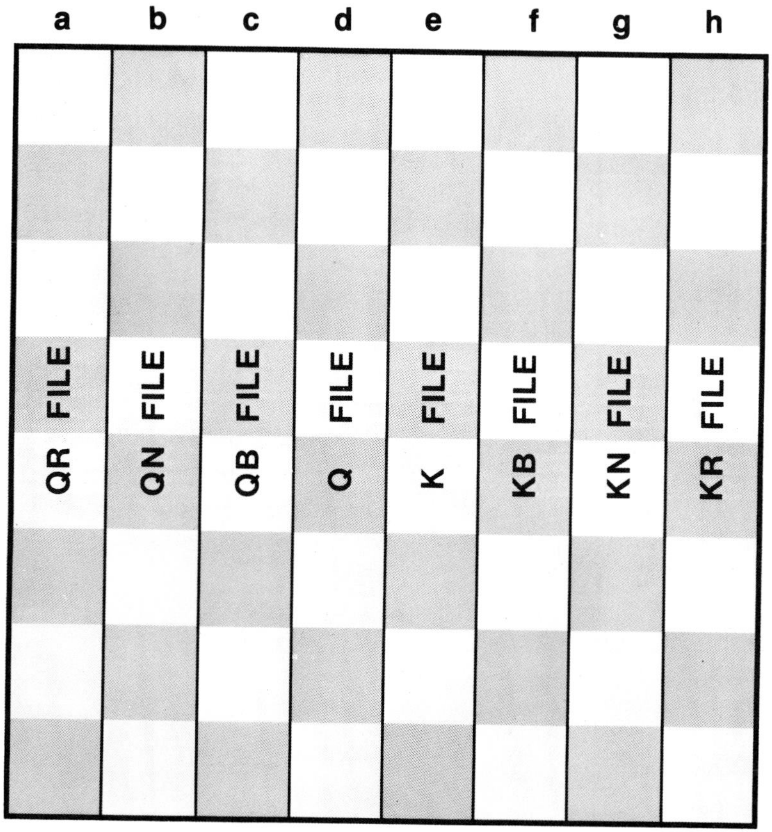

Fig. 2. The chessboard is organized into eight ranks for WHITE and, shown from the other side, for BLACK. WHITE's viewpoint of the board will always be assumed to coincide with that of the reader. BLACK will always sit on the opposite side of the board so that, if he were in the picture, he would be facing the reader. In the algebraic notation the ranks are labelled 1 to 8 as for WHITE in the descriptive notation. This is true regardless of whether WHITE or BLACK is making the move. Computers use the algebraic notation for the ranks.

Fig. 3. Each square on the chessboard is designated by citing the rank and file to which it belongs. In the descriptive notation, if WHITE is making the move, the squares are designated by the right-side-up symbols. If BLACK is moving, an up-side-down symbol designates the square. In the book BLACK's moves, when described in the descriptive notation, are printed in **bold-face type.** In the algebraic notation, the squares are designated a1, b1, . . . g8, h8 (as shown) regardless of whether WHITE or BLACK is making the move. Thus the arrow indicates square c8.

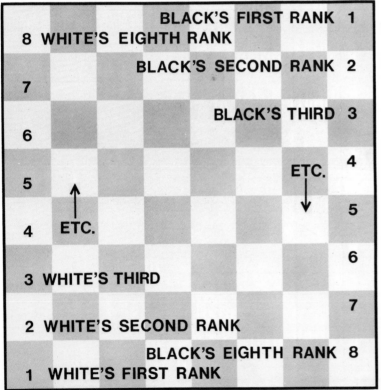

2. Seeing the Winning Move

During the course of a chess game, the chessmen at times occupy positions such that the player with the move can initiate a combination of moves against which his opponent is helpless to prevent checkmate. More often than not, however, these golden opportunities go unrecognized because (1) the player cannot see far enough ahead or (2) he suffers temporarily from chess blindness, a temporary inability to recognize a winning move that occasionally afflicts even seasoned players. Master players are much less subject to it than the rest of us. Moreover, they can see ahead for a greater number of moves and so recognize golden opportunities for which the winning combination is very subtle and perhaps many moves deep. The redoubtable Blackburne actually announced "mate in sixteen" and examples of announced "mate in ten" are not unusual. On the other hand, in *Chess Catechism* (Simon & Schuster, New York, 1970) Larry Evans cites an instance of a grandmaster resigning in a winning position!

On occasion, a winning combination of only a few moves may be more difficult to recognize than a long combination involving many moves. In such cases, the short combination probably begins with a highly imaginative move, one that is automatically rejected by an ordinary player because it seems pointless or even self-defeating at first glance. Such key moves are often overlooked when they involve a sacrifice of material, particularly of a Queen. To less-experienced players, giving up such material is almost unthinkable.

A player's ability to recognize winning combinations grows with his gifts of imagination and of *analysis*. In chess, analysis implies the ability to visualize chess moves without touching the chessmen. These gifts, although often innate, can be cultivated and expanded to a degree, particularly through above-the-board experience with players of equal or superior strength.

Studying published chess problems may also help. Many players like to study chess problems just before participation in tournament play, believing that it sharpens their perception. In these chess problems the chessmen may be intentionally arranged to camouflage the key move or to portray a chessboard at the point in an actual game when the player with the move has a winning position before him.

In order to help intermediate or less-experienced players learn to see winning moves the writer has collected from the literature and assembled here some problems that are not too complex, yet — especially in the later pages — become increasingly challenging. Many of these problems illustrate principles that will be of practical use in learning to analyze chess moves.

Moreover, the problems are illustrated by three-dimensional views of the board rather than by the conventional two-dimensional diagrams, and consequently more closely resemble actual chess playing situations. This should aid less-experienced players because, as Adriaan DeGroot noted in *Thought and Choice in Chess* (Mouton, The Hague, 1965), a lower-rated player's ability to visualize solutions increases if the problems are set up on a real board rather than being presented by the conventional diagrams. This is particularly true as the problems become more complicated. Therefore, by studying the problems presented here, a player should be able to sharpen his perception of winning moves in actual competition.

3. Engineering a Checkmate

For a King located near the board's center, nine squares are strategic: (a) the one he occupies and (b) the eight to which he may next move (Fig. 4). To be checkmated this King must be placed in check and must also be prevented from moving onto any of his eight next-move squares. Moves to these squares will be blocked if (1) they are controlled by enemy chessmen and/or (2) they are occupied by friendly chessmen. With his next-move squares so denied him, any check of this King thus checkmates him — provided this check cannot be relieved by capture of the man doing the checking or by interposition of a friendly chessman to shield the King from the attack.

The type of checkmate known as a *smothered mate* can occur if all the King's next-move squares are occupied by his own men. An enemy Knight can then threaten to leap over them and administer the *coup de grace* (Fig. 5). Typically, smothered mates occur when the King is near the corner of the board. In such a position his next-move squares are many fewer than eight. Of course, your opponent will never smother his King willingly. You must be alert for ways of forcing him into it. An example of this is given among the problems.

Sometimes the chessman that institutes the fatal check will simultaneously seal off the last of the King's next-move squares. For the Black King in Figure 6, all his next-move squares except those marked X are denied him. The White Queen, if moved to the square shown in Figure 7, achieves a checkmate because she checks the Black King and simultaneously attacks the squares marked X; all escape routes for the Black King are thus cut off.

It is helpful to keep in mind the next-move squares available to your opponent's King because it may suggest a means of checkmating him. Conversely, it is good to keep a wary eye on your opponent if he attempts to control the next-move squares of your King and thereby spin a web around him.

Fig. 4. The squares strategic to a King placed near the center of a chessboard are (1) the square he occupies and (2) the eight next-move squares around it. Checkmates of a King are usually preceded by careful analysis of the extent to which the King's eight next-move squares are denied him (because they are occupied by his own men or are controlled by enemy pieces). A checkmate of the King is achieved if (1) he cannot legally move onto any of his eight next-move squares and (2) he is at the same time placed under a check which cannot be relieved by either interposing a friendly piece or capturing the chessman checking him.

Fig. 5. In a smothered mate the King's next-move squares are denied him because all are occupied by friendly pieces. The White Knight would then move where shown to administer an un-relievable check of the Black King, who is smothered amid a crowd of friends.

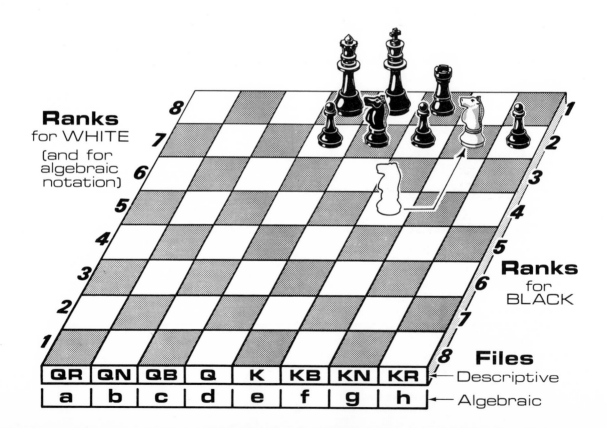

Ranks
for WHITE
(and for algebraic notation)

Ranks
for
BLACK

| QR | QN | QB | Q | K | KB | KN | KR | ← Descriptive |
| a | b | c | d | e | f | g | h | ← Algebraic |

Files

Fig. 6. The Black King seems in no trouble because he can move
onto any of the four next-move squares marked X.

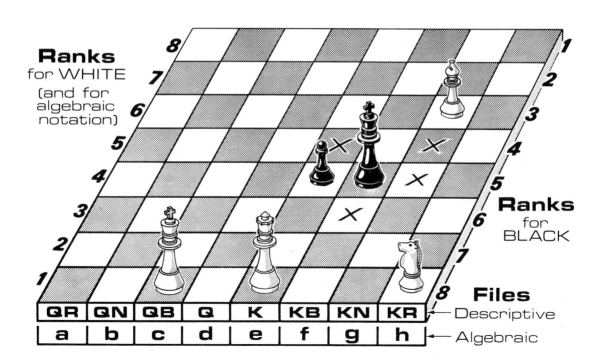

Fig. 7. The White Queen moves so as to check the Black King and at the same time seize control of the squares formerly marked *X*. The King cannot capture the White Queen, because she is protected by the White Knight. It is "curtains" for the Black King.

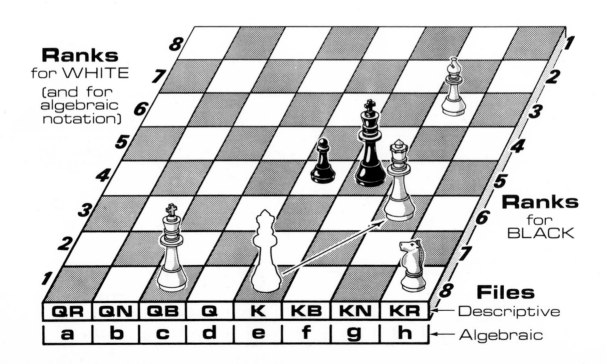

Ranks
for WHITE
(and for algebraic notation)

Ranks
for BLACK

Files

QR	QN	QB	Q	K	KB	KN	KR	← Descriptive
a	b	c	d	e	f	g	h	← Algebraic

4. United States Chess Federation Ratings

The game of golf would not be interesting without establishing a par for each hole. This gives the golfer something to shoot for. In a similar vein, the USCF ratings provide a way for a player to estimate the strength of his opponent. On a numerical scale these ratings range from below 1000 to well above 2000. Depending on their USCF rating, players in the United States are sometimes divided into the following classes of strength:

SENIOR MASTERS	Above 2399
MASTERS	2200 – 2399
EXPERTS	2000 – 2199
CLASS A	1800 – 1999
CLASS B	1600 – 1799
CLASS C	1400 – 1599
CLASS D	1200 – 1399
CLASS E	Below 1200

As of September 1972, after the world championship match, Bobby Fischer, whose uncanny judgment had brought him to the pinnacle of world chess, had a rating of 2810. The Russian contender, Boris Spassky, had a rating of 2704.

Recently, the World Chess Federation, whose official name is Federation Internationale des Echecs (FIDE), adopted the USCF rating system in modified form. The rating system has thus become international in scope.

The official procedures used by the USCF to assign ratings are described in its *Official Chess Handbook*, (David McKay, New York, 1972) which may be purchased from the Federation, 186 Route 9W, New Windsor, NY 12550. After an unrated player has played against rated players in a USCF-approved tournament, the (1) average USCF rating of his opponents and (2) percentage of games won from them are used to find his tentative rating from a special table in the *Official Chess Handbook.*

On the other hand, if two players with established ratings play and if W' and L', respectively, represent the ratings of the winner and loser before their match, then their new ratings (W and L) can be computed as follows:

$$W = W' + 16 + .04\,(L'-W') \qquad \text{(eq. 1)}$$
$$L = L' - 16 + .04\,(W'-L') \qquad \text{(eq. 2)}$$

Suppose a player rated 1800 defeated a player rated 1600. His new rating could be computed from Equation 1 to be 1808. Similarly, the new rating of the loser would be computed from Equation 2 as 1592.

For matches between players whose ratings differ by more than 350, only 350 can be substituted for $L'-W'$ (or $W'-L'$) in the equations. Thus if a player rated 1800 were defeated by a player rated 1200, his new rating would be $1800 - 16 - .04\,(350)$, or 1770.

5. Using the Mate-Raters

Each of the 14 mate-rater problems permits a reader to determine his own approximate USCF rating. To do so, he must time himself while solving the problem. The warm-up problem immediately preceding each mate-rater is specially marked so the reader will remember to slip a sheet of paper behind the page. In this way, he covers (and thus avoids seeing) the mate-rater on the right-hand page while checking the answer on the left-hand page to the preceding warm-up problem.

When ready to do the mate-rater problem:

(1) Remove the cover sheet
(2) Begin timing yourself with a stop watch, a dark room timer, or the sweep-second hand of the nearest available clock or watch. (If using a regular clock or watch make sure to note down the minute you started as well as the second)
(3) Solve the problem
(4) Record your solution in the blanks provided on the page or on a separate piece of paper
(5) Note the time and record that, too
(6) Check your answer on the following page
(7) If your answer is correct and the time it took you to find it was 10 minutes or less, use the accompanying table to find your approximate USCF rating

The tables are very easy to read. In the first column find the time you have marked down for the solution to the mate-rater. If your time was less than a minute, look up the seconds immediately; if your time was more than a minute you will have to convert it to seconds and then look it up in the table. For example, if it took you 8 minutes and 20 seconds to find the answer, look up 500 seconds on the table (8 x 60) + 20 = 500.

Next, find the approximate rating for this time. This is a good guess as to what your USCF rating would be on the basis of solving the mate-rater. The high and low figures show the range in which your rating might be likely to fall in two-thirds of the cases. In other words, it could be as high as the high figure shown, and it could be as low as the low figure shown.

USCF ratings are determined from a number of games played, therefore the average score on all the fourteen mate-raters gives a closer approximation to a reader's true standing than any single score. Because of the statistical analysis used, the average of all the fourteen approximate ratings will be within 150 points of the true USCF rating in the majority of the cases.

After averaging your scores, look back at the chart of classes of strength of players given on p. 24. Since each of these ranges covers 200 points you can make a very good guess, on the basis of the mate-raters, about what class you are in.

6. One-Move-to-Mate Problems

Experienced players may wish to skip these one-move problems and proceed immediately to the two-move problems (p. 52). None of the one-move problems tested on the rated players proved sufficiently challenging to the better players to be suitable as a mate-rater problem. Thus, the mate-raters first appear among the two-move problems. Less experienced players, however, may appreciate the following one-move problems as a transition (and preparation) for the two-move problems.

Problem 1

(a) WHITE to move and mate in one.
(b) If it is BLACK's move instead of WHITE's, what
   is BLACK's best move?

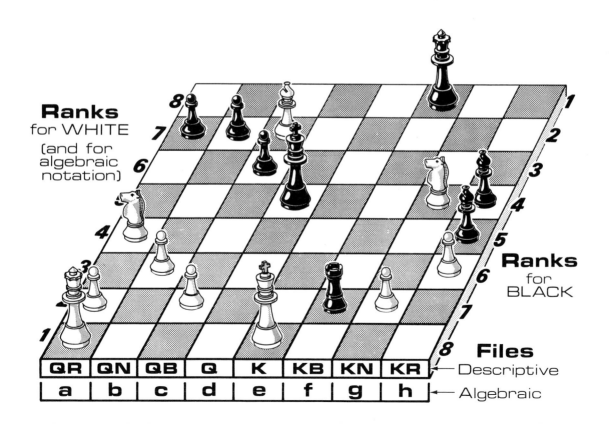

29

Answers to Problem 1

(a) Every available next-move square for the Black King is controlled by WHITE's Queen, his Bishop, or one of his Knights. Consequently, an irrefutable check by WHITE results in a checkmate. Thus,

     1.Q—K5 mate   *or*   1.P—QB4 mate   1. Qa1-e5 mate   *or* 1. c2-c4 mate

(b) Every available next-move square for the White King is controlled by BLACK's Rook or his Bishop (on **KR4**).* Hence,   *(on h5)

    1. . . .   **R** x P (either) mate   1. . . .   **R**f2x(c2 or g2)

produces a discovered check, and **soon** checkmate, by the Black Bishop patrolling the dark squares. Thus,

2. B-KN3   **B** x B mate   2. Bc7-g3   **B**h4xg3 mate

Problem 2

(a) WHITE to move and mate in one.
(b) If it is BLACK's move instead of WHITE's, what
    is BLACK's best move?

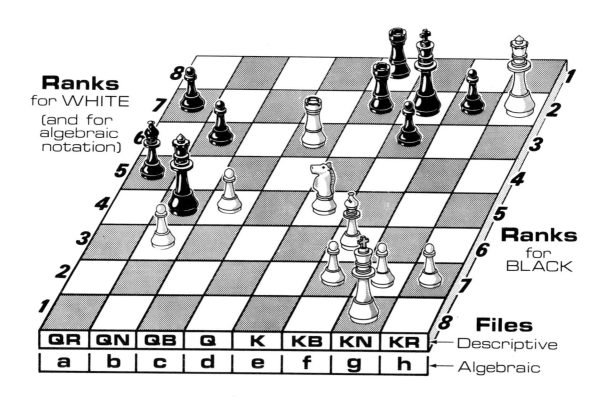

Answers to Problem 2

(a) WHITE observes that BLACK's Knight Pawn is securely pinned because moving this Pawn would illegally expose the Black King to check by the White Queen. He also notes that the Black King has only one available next-move square (**KB1**).* Thus,

*f8

<blockquote>1.R x BP mate</blockquote>

<blockquote>1. Rd6xf6 mate</blockquote>

The White Rook attacks the Black King as well as square **KB1,** his last available next-move square. BLACK cannot capture the White Rook with his Knight Pawn (it is pinned by the White Queen) or with his King (the White Knight now protects the White Rook).

(b)   1. . . .   **Q—K8** mate

1. . . .   Qb4-e1 mate

The White King suffers the ignominy of a *back-rank checkmate***which at some time or other befalls most beginning players.

**See Bloss, *Chess at a Glance* (New York: Van Nostrand Reinhold, 1967), for discussion of this on page 61, and for an introduction to other beginning techniques.

Problem 3

(a) WHITE to move and mate in one.
(b) If it is BLACK's move instead of WHITE's, what
    is BLACK's best move?

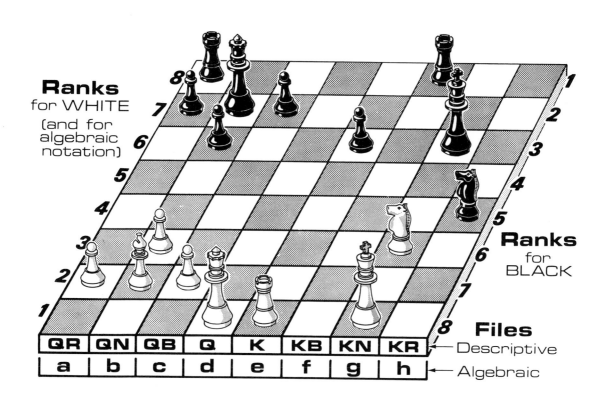

Answers to Problem 3

(a)   1.Q—KR5 mate   1. Qd1-h5 mate

The White Queen simultaneously attacks the
Black King and closes off all his next-move
squares, namely **KB4, KN4, KR3, KR2,** and   f5, g5, h6, h7, and f7
KB2.

(b)   1. . . .   **Q—KN7** mate   1. . . .   **Q**b7-g2 mate

Note that the Black Knight protects the Black
Queen from capture by the White King. This is a
recurring theme in chess; that is, a checkmate is
engineered by moving one's Queen onto a square
adjacent to the opposing King, who is at the edge
of the board. Moreover, when on this adjacent
square the Queen herself is protected by a friendly
piece from capture by the King struggling in her
deadly embrace.

Problem 4

WHITE to move and mate in one.

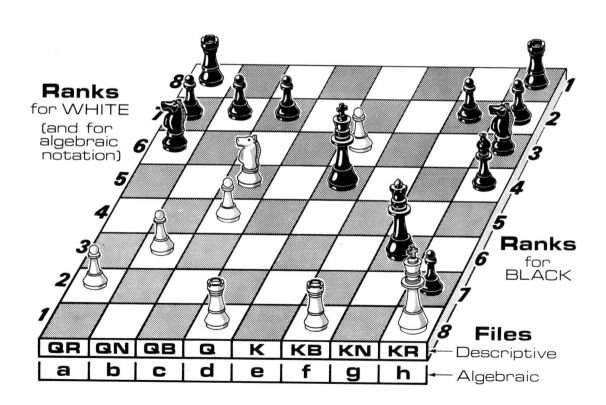

Ranks for WHITE (and for algebraic notation)

Ranks for BLACK

QR	QN	QB	Q	K	KB	KN	KR
a	b	c	d	e	f	g	h

Files ← Descriptive

← Algebraic

35

Answers to Problem 4

1. R−Q5 mate

Note that as the board is set in this problem the Black King has no next-move squares available to him. The move shown above retains control over the Black King's next-move squares on the Queen file while placing him in an irrefutable check.

1. Rdl-d5 mate

Problem 5

(a) WHITE to move and mate in one.
(b) If it is BLACK's move instead of WHITE's, what
    is BLACK's best move?

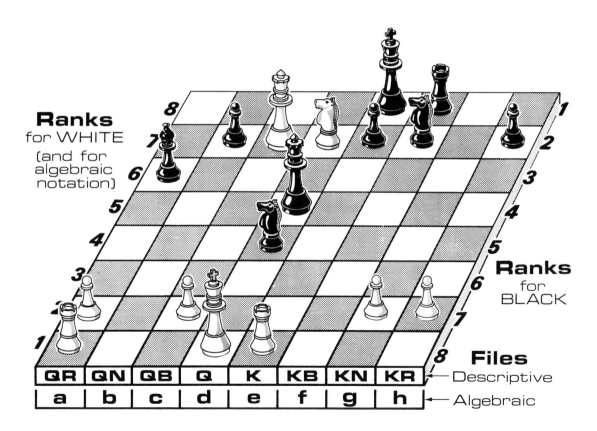

37

Answers to Problem 5

(a)   1. N−KB6, checkmate   1. Nd7-f6, checkmate

WHITE capitalizes on the fact that his Rook has pinned BLACK's King Pawn, which is consequently prevented from capturing the White Knight when he moves onto square KB6.*   *f6

(b)   1. . . .   **N−QN6,** checkmate   1. . . .   **N**d4-b3, checkmate

White's King succumbs to a discovered check by the Black Queen.

Problem 6

(a) WHITE to move and mate in one.
(b) If it is BLACK's move instead of WHITE's, what
    is BLACK's best move?

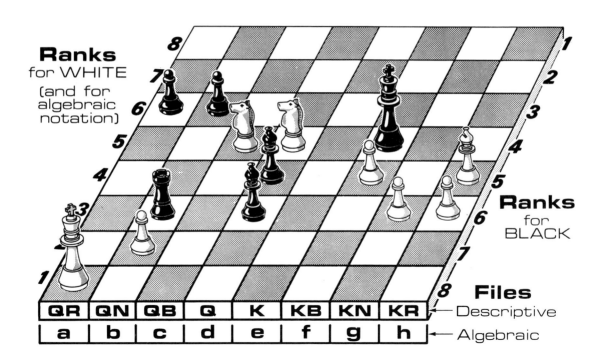

Ranks for WHITE (and for algebraic notation)

Ranks for BLACK

Files

QR	QN	QB	Q	K	KB	KN	KR	— Descriptive
a	b	c	d	e	f	g	h	— Algebraic

39

Answers to Problem 6

(a) All of the Black King's next-move squares, except for **KN3**,* are controlled by White chessmen. Thus,

                1.N−K7

  *g6

  1. Nd5-e7

checkmates BLACK because it seals off the Black King's last available next-move square **KN3** and, at the same time, administers the fatal check.

(b)   1. . . .   **R−QR6,** checkmate

  1. . . .   **R**b3-a3 mate

The Black Bishop pins the White Pawn so as to prevent him from capturing the attacking Black Rook.

Problem 7

(a) WHITE to move and mate in one.
(b) If it were BLACK's move instead of WHITE's, what is BLACK's best move?

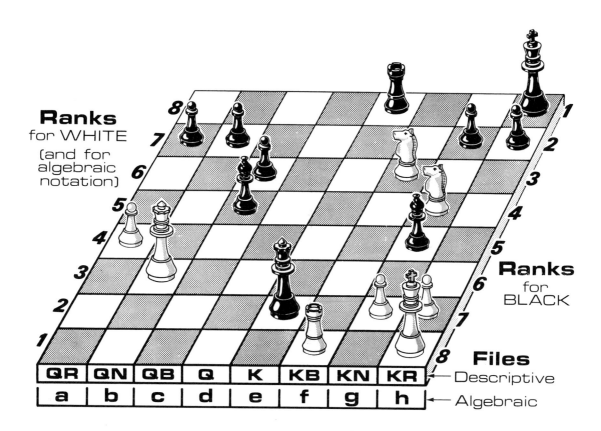

Answers to Problem 7

(a) The Black King, being at the corner of the board, has only three next-move squares. But two are occupied by his own Pawns and the third is controlled by one of the White Knights. The remaining White Knight thus can move

                    1.N−KB7 checkmate   1. Ng5-f7 mate

(b)   1. . . .   **Q** x R mate   1. . . .   **Qe2xf1 mate**

Problem 8

(a) WHITE to move and mate in one.
(b) If it were BLACK's move instead of WHITE's,
give his best move(s).

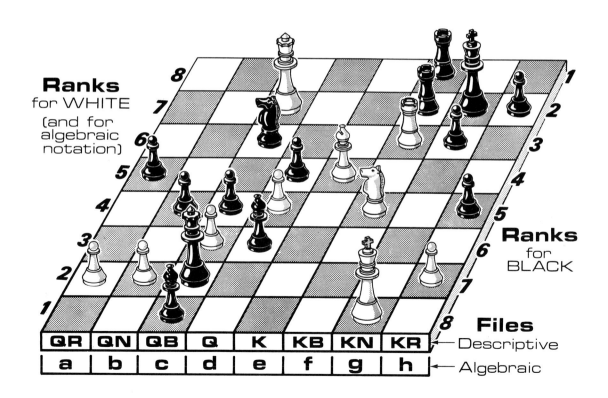

QR	QN	QB	Q	K	KB	KN	KR	← Descriptive
a	b	c	d	e	f	g	h	← Algebraic

43

Answers to Problem 8

(a)   1.R x P mate

WHITE here subjects the Black King to a devastating double check; that is, a check by the White Rook and a discovered check by the White Bishop. In a twinkling all the Black King's next-move squares are denied him and he is subjected to a fatal check. Note that *a double check always includes a discovered check.* Thus, with the board as set in Problem 8, WHITE has a cocked pistol (the White Bishop) aimed at the Black King. The White Rook, seemingly benevolently shielding the Black King from attack by this White Bishop, is actually the trigger of the cocked pistol.

(b) With a cocked pistol pointing at his King, BLACK must make moves to which WHITE's replies are forced. Forced moves are those a player has to make to save his King from immediate capture. Thus,

1. . . .	**B − K6** ch
2.K − KR1	**B − K5** ch
3.N − KN2	**Q** x N mate

1. Rf6xg6 mate

1. . . .	**B**c1-e3 +
2. Kg1-h1	**B**d3-e4 +
3. Nf4-g2	**Q**c2xg2 mate

44

Problem 9

WHITE to move and mate in one.

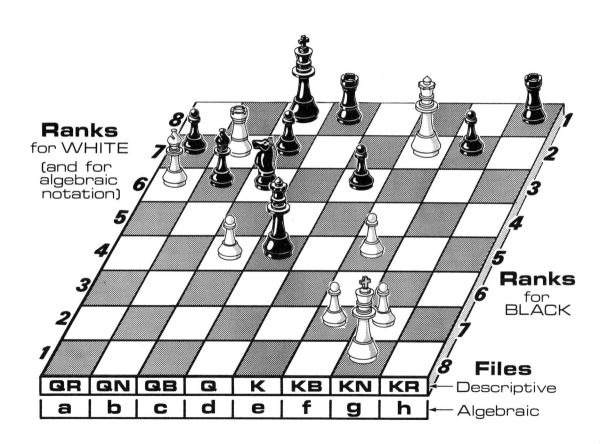

QR	QN	QB	Q	K	KB	KN	KR	← Descriptive
a	b	c	d	e	f	g	h	← Algebraic

45

Answer to Problem 9

1.R x **B** mate

The discovered check by the White Bishop finishes the Black King.

Originally tested to see if it could be a mate-rater, this problem was missed by four of the tested players, two of them having ratings in excess of 1700. Undoubtedly these were instances of chess blindness.

1. Rb7xb6 mate

Problem 10

WHITE to move and mate in one.

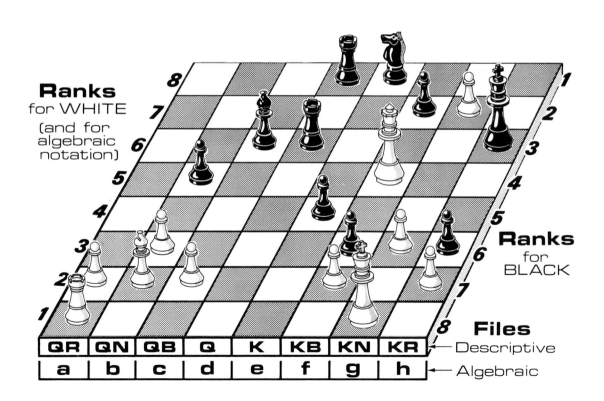

Ranks
for WHITE
(and for
algebraic
notation)

Ranks
for
BLACK

QR	QN	QB	Q	K	KB	KN	KR	Descriptive
a	b	c	d	e	f	g	h	Algebraic

Files

47

Answer to Problem 10

1.P—KN8(N) mate

The possibility of underpromotion of the Pawn to a Knight instead of to a Queen seemed to elude some of the less experienced players. Although this problem failed to qualify as a mate-rater, four of the tested players with ratings below 1500 failed to solve it.

1. g7-g8(N) mate

Problem 11

WHITE to move and mate in one.

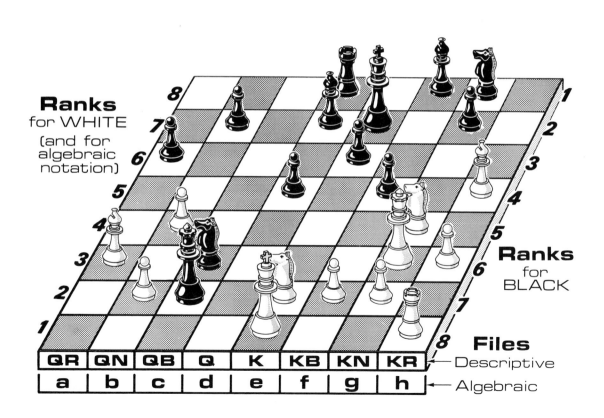

Answer to Problem 11

The White Bishop on square KR5*and the White Knight on square KN4**control all but one of the Black King's next-move squares. Thus,

                1.P—QN5 mate

represents the *coup de grace* in the form of a discovered check by the White Bishop on QR3.***

*h5

**g4

1. b4-b5 mate

***a3

7. Two-Move Problems

In this section, problems, 20, 25, 30, 35, 40, 45, 50, and 55 are mate-rater problems. If the reader desires to determine his approximate USCF rating by timing himself on these he should slip a sheet of paper behind the problem immediately preceding each mate-rater. For example, a sheet of paper inserted immediately behind Problem 19 will prevent the reader from inadvertently seeing Mate-Rater 20 while checking his solution to Problem 19.

Problem 12

WHITE to move and mate in two.

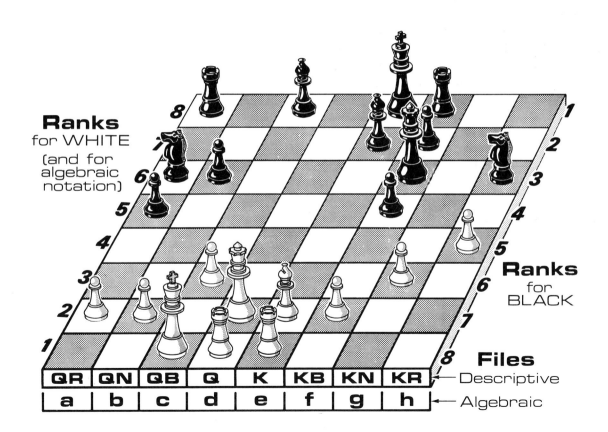

Answer to Problem 12

1.Q−Q8 ch	**B** x Q
2.B−QN5 mate	

1. Qd2-d8 +	**B**e7xd8
2. Be2-b5 mate	

WHITE sacrifices his Queen to set up that most potent of chess weapons, a double check. After 2.B−QN5 dbl ch, the Black King is simultaneously attacked by WHITE's Rook and Bishop. There is no escape. Note that a double check involves a move by a chessman who gives check — the Bishop in this case — and that this move unleashes the action of another piece — in this case, the Rook — so that it also gives check.

Problem 13

WHITE to move and win in two.

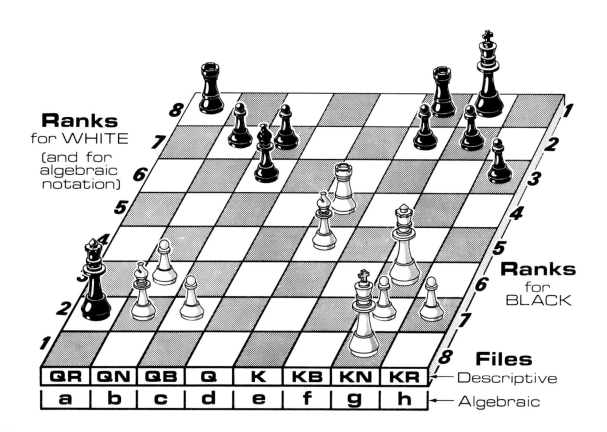

| QR | QN | QB | Q | K | KB | KN | KR | ← Descriptive |
| a | b | c | d | e | f | g | h | ← Algebraic |

55

Answer to Problem 13

1.Q x **P,** ch!   **K** x Q

WHITE sacrifices his Queen to set up an un-answerable double check. Thus,

2.R−KN5 mate

1. Qg3xg7 +!   **K**g8xg7

2. Re5-g5 mate

Problem 14

(a) WHITE to move and win in two.
(b) If it were BLACK's move instead of WHITE's, give BLACK's best move.

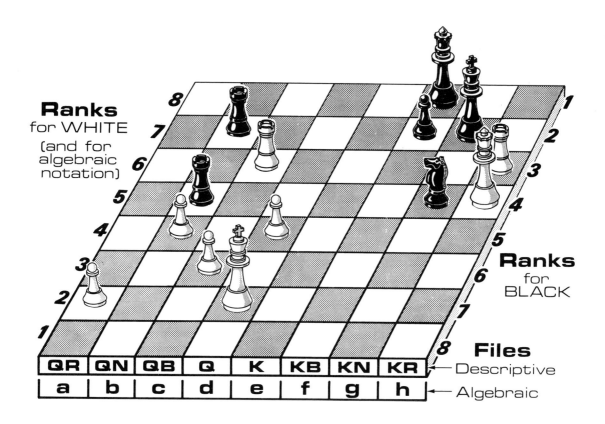

Answers to Problem 14

(a)   1.R(at QB6)−KN6, ch   **P** x R   1. Rc6-g6 +   f7xg6

            2.Q x **P** mate   2. Qh5xg6 mate

(b)   1. . . .   **N**−K5 ch   1. . . .   **N**g5-e4 +

With this move the Black Knight checks WHITE's King and simultaneously initiates a discovered attack by the Black Rook on the White Queen. WHITE has to move his King, whereupon BLACK exchanges his Rook for the White Queen.

Problem 15

(a) WHITE to move and win in two.
(b) If it were BLACK's move instead of WHITE's,
give his best move.

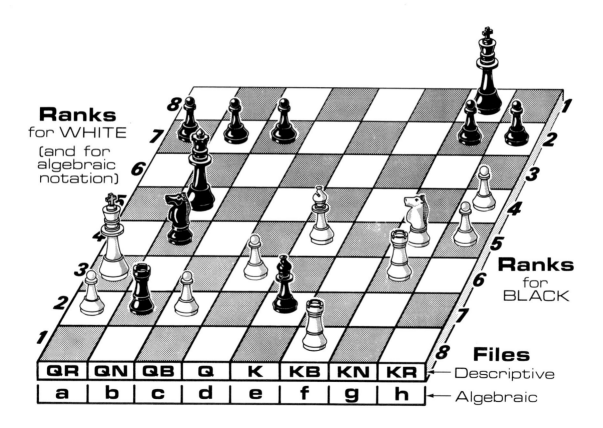

Answers to Problem 15

(a) 1. N−KR6 ch   **K−R1**   1. Ng4-h6 +   **K**g8-h8
       2. R−KB8 mate   2. Rf1-f8 mate

(b) 1. . . .   **N** x P (on **QB7**) mate   1. . . .   **N**b4xc2 mate

Problem 16

WHITE to move and win in two.

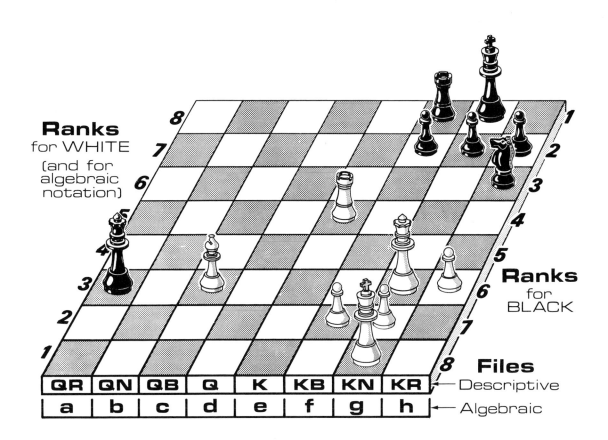

Ranks
for WHITE
(and for
algebraic
notation)

Ranks
for
BLACK

Files

QR	QN	QB	Q	K	KB	KN	KR	— Descriptive
a	b	c	d	e	f	g	h	— Algebraic

61

Answer to Problem 16

1. Q x P ch   K x Q

2. R−KN5 mate

Being essentially a repeat of Problem 13, this should have taken only a short time to solve.

1. Qg3xg7 +   Kg8xg7

2. Re5-g5 mate

Problem 17

WHITE to move and win in two.

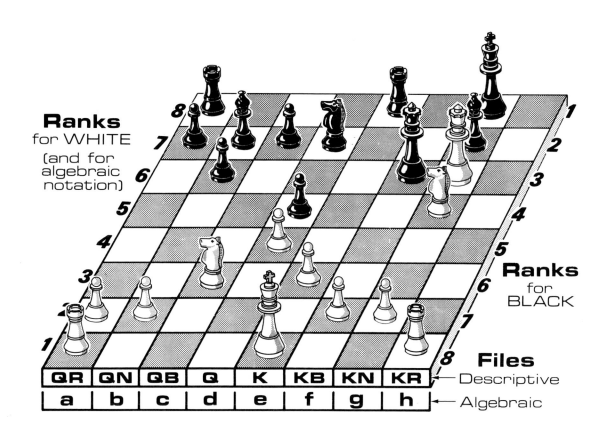

Ranks
for WHITE
(and for
algebraic
notation)

8
7
6
5
4
3
2
1

Ranks
for
BLACK

1
2
3
4
5
6
7
8

Files

| QR | QN | QB | Q | K | KB | KN | KR | ← Descriptive |
| a | b | c | d | e | f | g | h | ← Algebraic |

63

Answer to Problem 17

1. R — KR8 ch   **K** x R
2. Q — KR7 mate

1. Rh1-h8 +   **K**g8xh8
2. Qg6-h7 mate

Warm-Up Problem 18

WHITE to move and win in two.

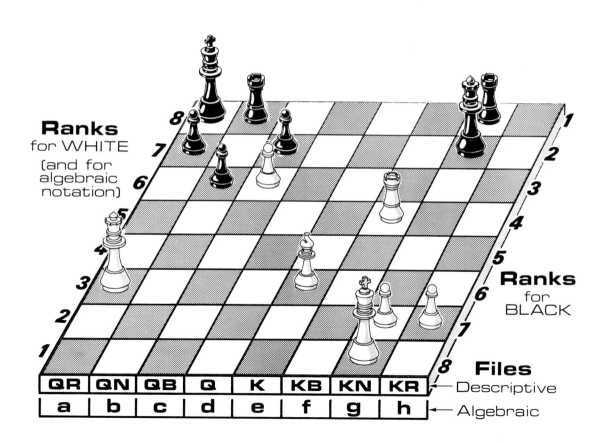

Answer to Problem 18

1.Q x **P** ch!   **K** x Q

This puts the Black King on the White Bishop's line of fire, BLACK's Knight Pawn now being pinned so that

2.R—QR5 mate

Except for two players with USCF rating of 1400 or less, all of the rated players solved this quickly and correctly. One player rated 1216 solved it in 20 seconds. On the other hand, one experienced player with a 1725 rating took 7 minutes and 50 seconds. Results were too erratic for this to be a mate-rater.

1. Qa3xa7 +!   **Ka8x7**

2. Rf5-a5 mate

Warm-Up Problem 19

The problem that follows is a mate-rater. To avoid seeing it while checking the answers to this problem, insert a sheet of paper behind this page.

(a) WHITE to move and win in two.
(b) If it were BLACK's move instead of WHITE's, give his best move(s).

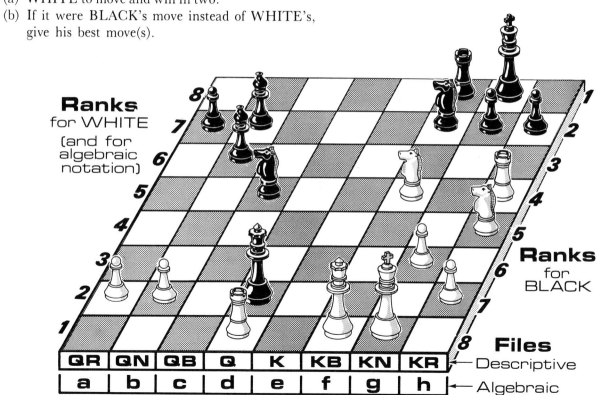

Answers to Problem 19

(a) 1. N−K7 ch   **K−R1**   1. Nf5-e7 +   **Kg8-h8**

      2. N(at KR4)−N6 mate   2. Nh4-g6 mate

Not a single rated player missed WHITE's move.

(b) 1. . . .   **N−Q6** dis ch   1. . . .   **N**c5-d3 +

      2. N−K3   **B** x N ch   2. Nf5-e3   **B**b6xe3 +

      3. Q−KB2   **Q** x Q mate   3. Qf1-f2   **Q**d2xf2 mate

Mate-Rater Problem 20

WHITE to move and win in two.

1. _____   _____
2. _____ mate Time required:

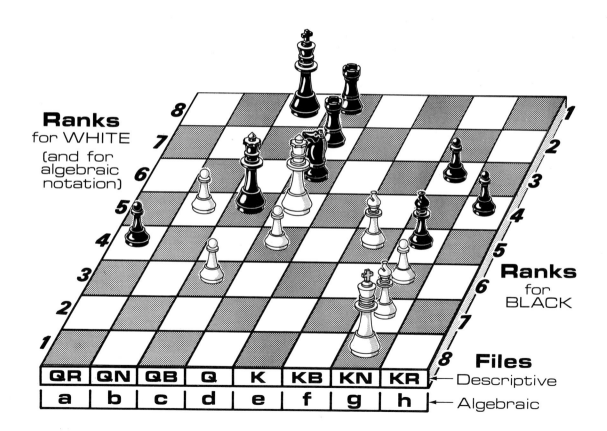

Answer to Problem 20

    1.Q–QR8 ch   **K–B2**
    2.Q–N7 mate

If your answer is correct and the time required for solution was 10 minutes (or less), your approximate USCF rating, as well as a lower and a higher USCF rating between which your USCF rating is likely to fall, will appear adjacent to your solution time in the table which follows. Remember that you have to convert your solution-time to seconds.

    1. Qd5-a8 +   **K**c8-c7
    2. Qa8-b7 mate

Table for Mate-Rater 20

time (sec)	rating	low	high	time (sec)	rating	low	high
5	1981	1800	2179	310	1382	1256	1521
10	1865	1695	2051	320	1378	1253	1516
20	1755	1595	1931	330	1375	1249	1512
30	1694	1540	1864	340	1371	1246	1508
40	1652	1502	1818	350	1368	1243	1505
50	1621	1473	1783	360	1364	1240	1501
60	1595	1450	1755	370	1361	1237	1497
70	1574	1430	1731	380	1358	1234	1494
80	1555	1414	1711	390	1355	1231	1490
90	1540	1399	1694	400	1352	1229	1487
100	1526	1387	1678	410	1349	1226	1484
110	1513	1375	1664	420	1346	1223	1481
120	1501	1365	1652	430	1343	1221	1478
130	1491	1355	1640	440	1341	1219	1475
140	1481	1346	1630	450	1338	1216	1472
150	1473	1338	1620	460	1335	1214	1469
160	1464	1331	1611	470	1333	1212	1466
170	1457	1324	1602	480	1330	1209	1464
180	1449	1317	1594	490	1328	1207	1461
190	1442	1311	1587	500	1326	1205	1458
200	1436	1305	1580	510	1323	1203	1456
210	1430	1300	1573	520	1321	1201	1454
220	1424	1294	1567	530	1319	1199	1451
230	1419	1289	1561	540	1317	1197	1449
240	1413	1285	1555	550	1315	1195	1446
250	1408	1280	1549	560	1313	1193	1444
260	1404	1276	1544	570	1311	1191	1442
270	1399	1272	1539	580	1309	1190	1440
280	1395	1267	1534	590	1307	1188	1438
290	1390	1264	1529	600	1305	1186	1435
300	1386	1260	1525				

Problem 21

WHITE to move and win in two.

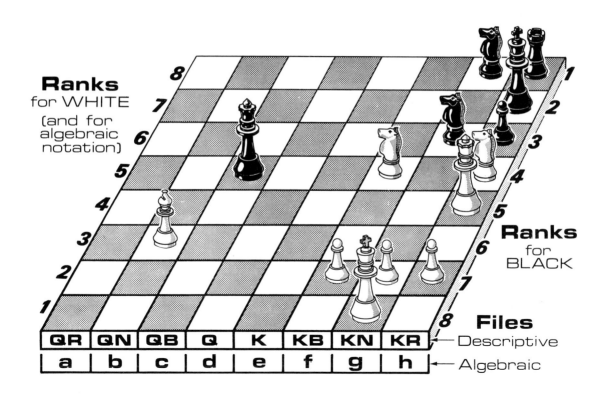

| QR | QN | QB | Q | K | KB | KN | KR | — Descriptive |
| a | b | c | d | e | f | g | h | — Algebraic |

Ranks
for WHITE
(and for
algebraic
notation)

Ranks
for
BLACK

Files

If WHITE is familiar with the Knight's peculiar inability to attack chessmen located on every second square along the diagonals on which this Knight stands, then he can immediately eliminate the White Knight on KB5 from any plans for checking the Black King. (For an analysis of the Knight's inabilities and capabilities see *Chess at a Glance*, p. 27.) WHITE faces a back-rank mate by BLACK and, furthermore, his Queen and Knight are both *en prise* — that is, subject to immediate capture by BLACK. Hence WHITE can only make *forcing moves*, which are moves which give check to the Black King. Thus,

1.N−KB6 ch	N x N
2.Q x **P** mate	

1. Nh5-f6 +	Ng8xf6
2. Qh4xh6 mate	

Note that 1.N−KB6 ch forces BLACK to remove his own Knight's protection from the Black Pawn and simultaneously initiates a discovered attack by the White Queen on this Black Pawn.

Problem 22

(a) WHITE to move and win in two.
(b) If it were BLACK's move instead of WHITE's,
    give his best move(s).

Answers to Problem 22

(a) 1.R−QR4 ch   **P** x R
    2.P−QN4 mate

(b) 1. . . .   **Q − Q4** mate

1. Rh4-a4 +   b5xa4
2. b3-b4 mate

1. . . .   **Q**f7-d5 mate

Warm-Up Problem 23

WHITE to move and win in two.

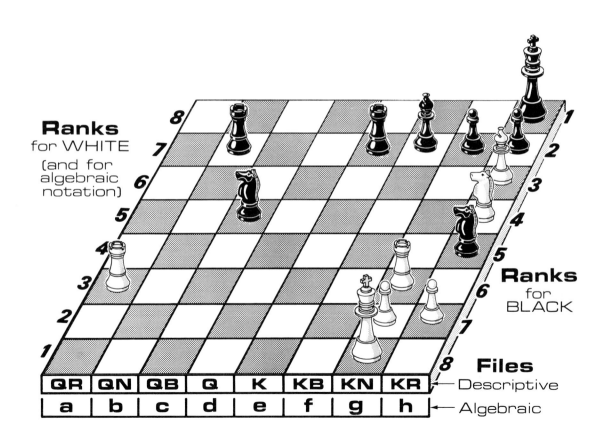

Answer to Problem 23

1. B x P ch   **K – N1**
2. N – B6 mate

1. Bh6xg7 +   **K**h8-g8
2. Nh5-f6 mate

Warm-Up Problem 24

Insert sheet behind this page to cover Mate-Rater Problem 25, which follows.

BLACK to move and win in two.
This situation occurred during a U.S. Open Championship game. WHITE has two passed Pawns and is a Rook up. The stage is virtually set for BLACK's annihilation. All BLACK has is the move, but that's enough. He wins in two.

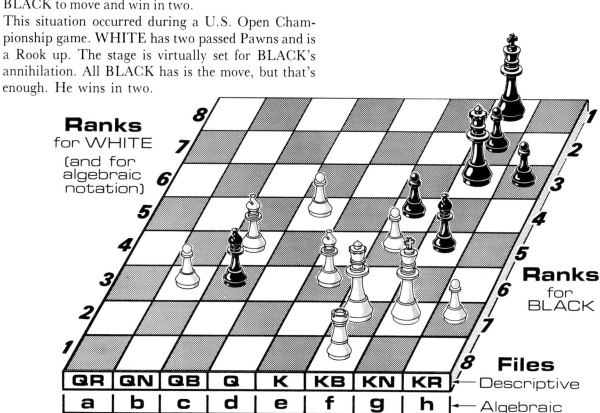

1. . . .   **B** – **B6** dbl ch

2. $\begin{cases} \text{K} \times \textbf{B} \\ \text{or} \\ \text{K} - \text{R3} \end{cases}$ **Q** – **KN5** mate

1. . . .   **B**g4-f3 ++

2. $\begin{cases} \text{Kg2xf3} \\ \text{or} \\ \text{Kg2-h3} \end{cases}$ **Q**g6-g4 mate

Mate-Rater Problem 25

WHITE to move and win in two.

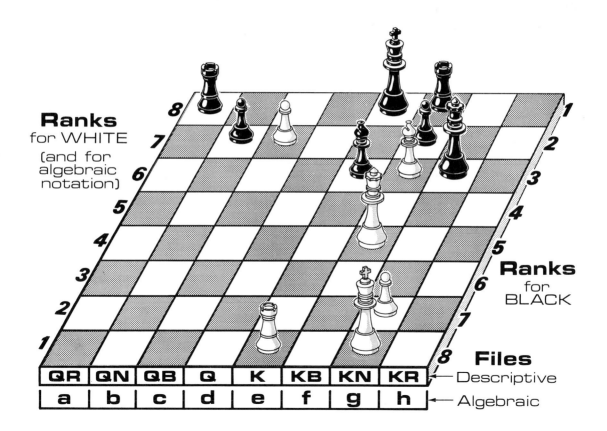

Ranks
for WHITE
(and for
algebraic
notation)

Ranks
for BLACK

Files

QR	QN	QB	Q	K	KB	KN	KR
a	b	c	d	e	f	g	h

Descriptive

Algebraic

Answer to Problem 25

       1.Q−QR4 ch   **R** x Q
       2.P−QB8(Q) mate

If, instead of 1. . . . **R** x Q, BLACK moves 1. . . . **P−QN4**, then 2.Q x **P** mate* If you had the correct answer in 10 minutes or less, determine your approximate USCF rating using the table that follows.

     1. Qf4-a4 +   **R**a8xa4
     2. c7-c8 (Q) mate

*If 1. . . . b7-b5, then 2. Qa4xb5 mate.

Table for Mate-Rater 25

time (sec)	rating	low	high	time (sec)	rating	low	high
5	2135	2002	2277	310	1392	1305	1485
10	1987	1863	2119	320	1388	1301	1480
20	1849	1734	1972	330	1383	1297	1475
30	1773	1662	1891	340	1379	1293	1471
40	1721	1614	1835	350	1375	1289	1466
50	1682	1577	1794	360	1371	1285	1462
60	1650	1547	1760	370	1367	1281	1458
70	1624	1523	1732	380	1363	1278	1454
80	1602	1502	1708	390	1359	1274	1450
90	1582	1484	1688	400	1356	1271	1446
100	1565	1468	1669	410	1352	1268	1442
110	1550	1453	1653	420	1349	1265	1439
120	1536	1440	1638	430	1346	1262	1435
130	1523	1428	1625	440	1342	1259	1432
140	1512	1417	1612	450	1339	1256	1428
150	1501	1407	1601	460	1336	1253	1425
160	1491	1398	1590	470	1333	1250	1422
170	1482	1389	1580	480	1330	1247	1419
180	1473	1381	1571	490	1328	1245	1416
190	1465	1373	1562	500	1325	1242	1413
200	1457	1366	1554	510	1322	1240	1410
210	1449	1359	1546	520	1319	1237	1407
220	1442	1352	1538	530	1317	1235	1404
230	1436	1346	1531	540	1314	1232	1402
240	1430	1340	1525	550	1312	1230	1399
250	1423	1335	1518	560	1309	1228	1396
260	1418	1329	1512	570	1307	1225	1394
270	1412	1324	1506	580	1305	1223	1391
280	1407	1319	1500	590	1302	1221	1389
290	1402	1314	1495	600	1300	1219	1386
300	1397	1310	1490				

Problem 26

WHITE to move and win in two.

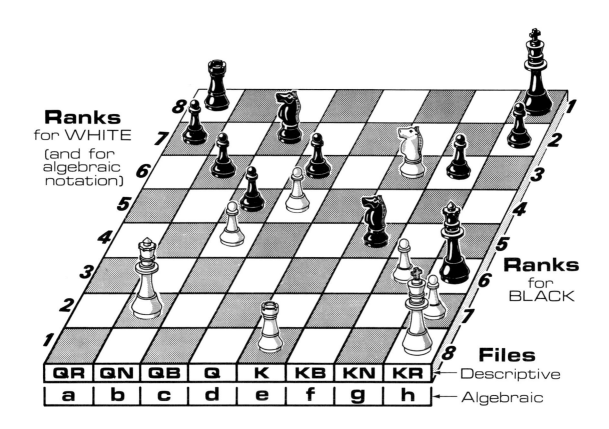

Ranks for WHITE (and for algebraic notation)								Ranks for BLACK

QR	QN	QB	Q	K	KB	KN	KR	← Descriptive
a	b	c	d	e	f	g	h	← Algebraic

Files

Answer to Problem 26

1. N—KR5 (or N—K8) dis ch   **K—N1**   1. Nf6-(h5 or e8) +   **Kh8-g8**
2. Q—KN7 mate   2. Qb2-g7 mate

Problem 27

WHITE to move and win in two.

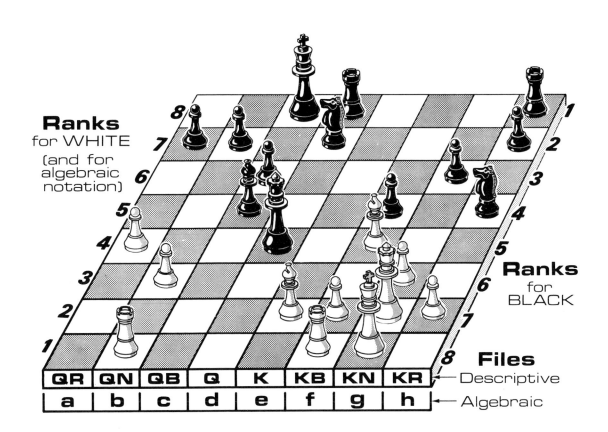

Ranks
for WHITE
(and for
algebraic
notation)

Ranks
for
BLACK

Files

| QR | QN | QB | Q | K | KB | KN | KR | ← Descriptive |
| a | b | c | d | e | f | g | h | ← Algebraic |

83

Answer to Problem 27

1.Q x **P** ch	**P** x Q	1. Qg2xc6 +	b7xc6
2.B—QR6 mate		2. Be2-a6 mate	

Warm-Up Problem 28

WHITE to move and win in two.
All the tested players, except one whose USCF rating
was less than 1200, found this easy.

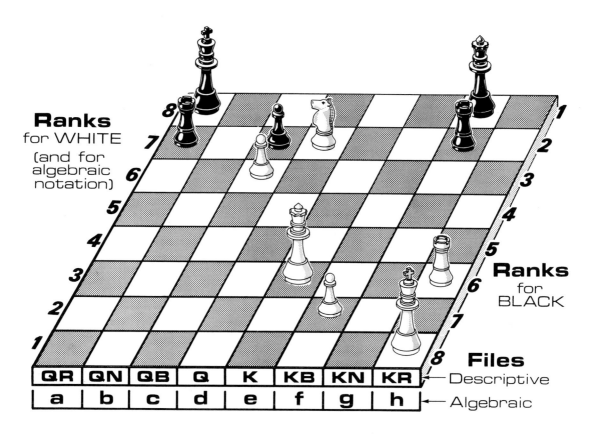

Ranks
for WHITE
(and for
algebraic
notation)

Ranks
for
BLACK

Files

QR	QN	QB	Q	K	KB	KN	KR
a	b	c	d	e	f	g	h

Descriptive

Algebraic

Answer to Problem 28

1. Q x **R** ch   **K** x Q
2. R — QR3 mate

1. Qe3xa7 +   **K**a8xa7
2. Rh3-a3 mate

Warm-Up Problem 29

Insert sheet behind this page to cover Mate-Rater Problem 30, which follows.

WHITE to move and win in two.

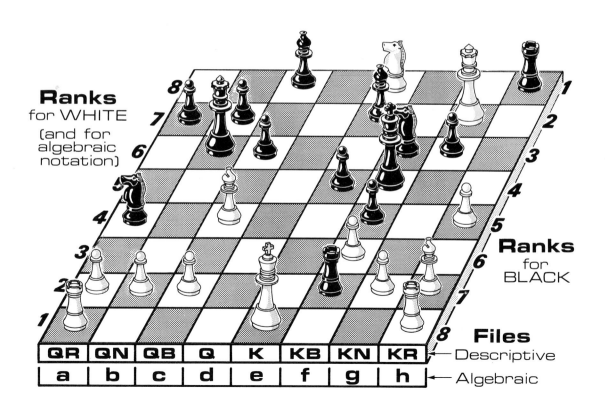

Answer to Problem 29

This problem stumped over one-third of the tested players including one with a USCF rating above 1900.

1.Q x **N** ch!	**B** x Q
2.N – Q6 mate	

1. Qg7xf6 +!	**B**e7xf6
2. Ne8-d6 mate	

Mate-Rater Problem 30

WHITE to move and win in two.

1. _____ _____
2. _____ mate Time required:

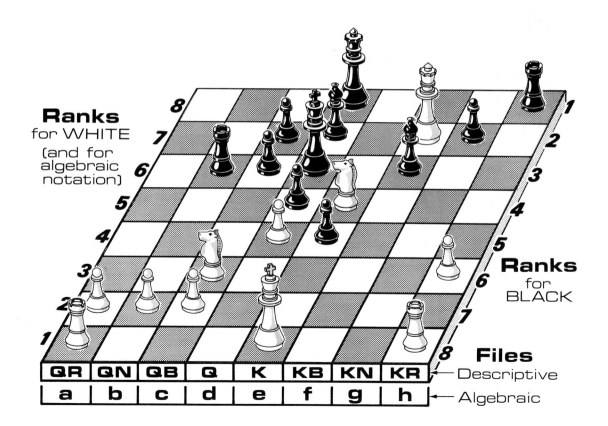

Ranks
for WHITE
(and for
algebraic
notation)

Ranks
for
BLACK

Files

| QR | QN | QB | Q | K | KB | KN | KR | ← Descriptive |
| a | b | c | d | e | f | g | h | ← Algebraic |

Answer to Problem 30

| 1.N x **KP** ch | P x N |
| 2.N−QB4 mate | |

or

| 1.N−QB4 ch | P x N |
| 2.N x **KP** mate | |

Of the tested players only 12% missed this. The highest rating to miss was 1556. If your solution was correct, use the following table to determine the approximate USCF rating at which you performed.

| 1. Nc3xe4 + | d5xe4 |
| 2. Ne5-c4 mate | |

or

| 1. Ne5-c4 + | d5xc4 |
| 2. Nc3xe4 mate | |

time (sec)	rating	low	high	time (sec)	rating	low	high
5	2194	2020	2383	310	1431	1317	1554
10	2042	1880	2218	320	1426	1313	1549
20	1900	1750	2064	330	1421	1309	1544
30	1822	1678	1980	340	1417	1305	1539
40	1769	1628	1921	350	1413	1301	1535
50	1728	1591	1877	360	1409	1297	1530
60	1696	1561	1842	370	1405	1293	1526
70	1669	1537	1813	380	1401	1290	1522
80	1646	1516	1788	390	1397	1286	1518
90	1626	1497	1767	400	1393	1283	1514
100	1609	1481	1747	410	1390	1280	1510
110	1593	1466	1730	420	1386	1276	1506
120	1578	1453	1715	430	1383	1273	1502
130	1565	1441	1701	440	1380	1270	1499
140	1553	1430	1688	450	1376	1267	1495
150	1542	1420	1676	460	1373	1264	1492
160	1532	1411	1664	470	1370	1262	1489
170	1523	1402	1654	480	1367	1259	1485
180	1514	1393	1644	490	1364	1256	1482
190	1505	1386	1635	500	1362	1253	1479
200	1497	1378	1626	510	1359	1251	1476
210	1490	1371	1618	520	1356	1248	1473
220	1482	1365	1610	530	1353	1246	1470
230	1476	1358	1603	540	1351	1244	1467
240	1469	1353	1596	550	1348	1241	1465
250	1463	1347	1589	560	1346	1239	1462
260	1457	1341	1583	570	1343	1237	1459
270	1451	1336	1577	580	1341	1234	1456
280	1446	1331	1571	590	1338	1232	1454
290	1441	1326	1565	600	1336	1230	1451
300	1436	1322	1559				

Problem 31

(a) WHITE to move and win in two.
(b) If it were BLACK's move instead of WHITE's,
   gives his best move.

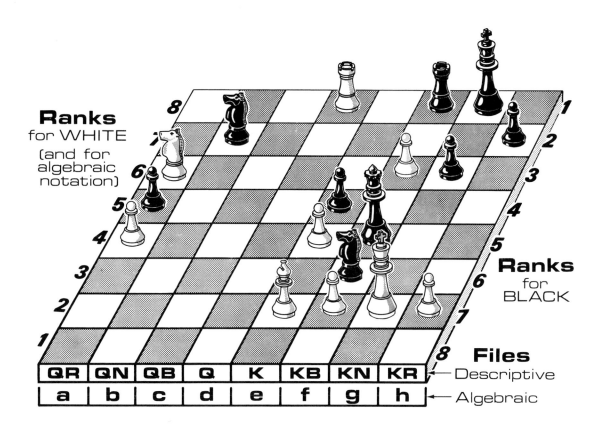

Ranks
for WHITE
(and for
algebraic
notation)

Ranks
for BLACK

Files

QR	QN	QB	Q	K	KB	KN	KR	— Descriptive
a	b	c	d	e	f	g	h	— Algebraic

Answers to Problem 31

(a)   1. B−QB4 ch   **K − R1**   1. Be2-c4 +   **K**g8-h8

          2. R x **R** mate   2. Rd8xt8 mate

(b)   1. . . . .   **Q** x RP ch   1. . . . .   **Q**f4xh2 +

          2. K x **N**   **Q − R6** mate   2. Kg2xf3   **Q**h2-h3 mate

          or   *or*

          2. K−KB1   **Q − R8** mate   2. Kg2-f1   Qh2-h1 mate

          or   *or*

          1. . . . .   **Q-N5** ch   1. . . . .   **Q**f4-g4 +

          2. K-(R1 or B1)   **Q-N8** mate   2. Kg2-(f1 or n1)   Qg4-g1 mate

Problem 32

WHITE to move and win in two.

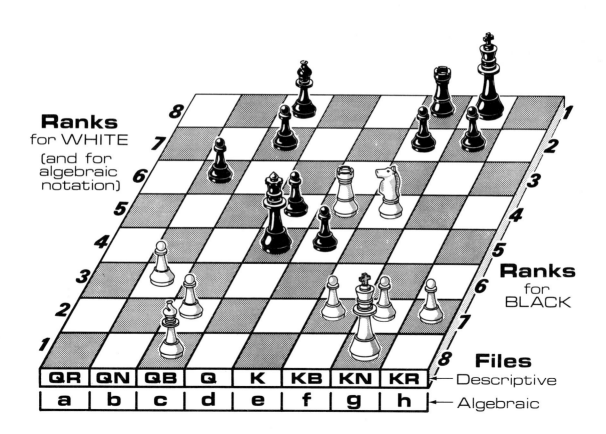

| QR | QN | QB | Q | K | KB | KN | KR | ← Descriptive |
| a | b | c | d | e | f | g | h | ← Algebraic |

93

1.N−K7 ch	**K−R2**	1. Nf5-e7 +	**K**g8-h7 (or h8)
2.R−KR5 mate		2.Re5-h5 mate	

WHITE had to maintain pressure on the Black King because he faced a back-rank checkmate the minute he stopped checking the Black King and permitted BLACK to move **Q−Q8** mate.*

*Qd4-d1 mate.

Problem 33

(a) WHITE to move and win in two.
(b) If it were BLACK's move, give his best move(s).

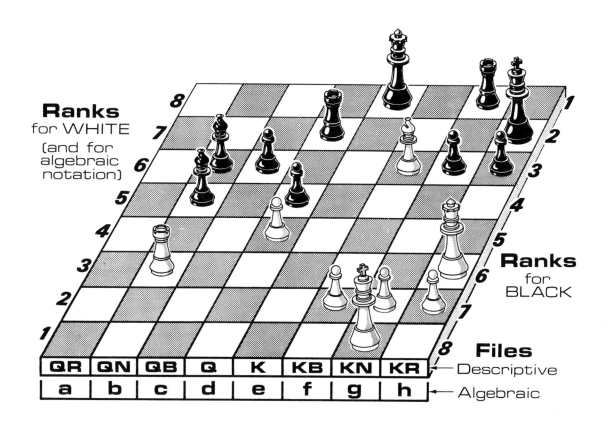

Answers to Problem 33

(a)   1.Q x **P** ch   **K** x Q   1. Qh3xh6 +   **K**h7xh6

            2.R − KR3 mate   2. Rb3-h3 mate

(b)   1. . . .   **Q−K8** mate   1. . . . .   Qe8-e1 mate

Warm-Up Problem 34

Insert a sheet of paper behind this page to conceal Mate-Rater
Problem 35, which follows.

WHITE to move and win in two.

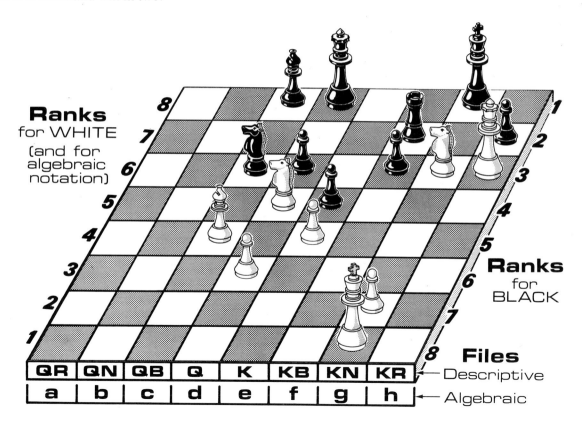

Answer to Problem 34

| 1.N x **BP** ch | **Q** x N | 1. Nd5xf6 + | Qd8xf6 |
| 2.Q—B8 mate | | 2. Qh6-f8 mate | |

Only 4 of the tested players missed this. By coincidence, their USCF ratings were all clustered between 1450 and 1550.

Mate-Rater Problem 35

WHITE to move and win in two.

1. _____ _____
2. _____ mate Time required:

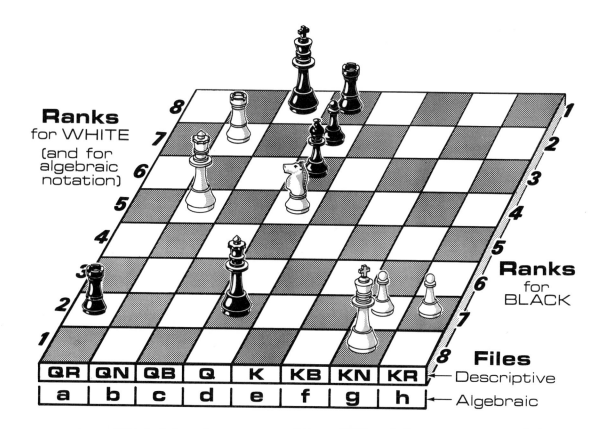

Answer to Problem 35

The theme of Problem 35 is similar to that in Problem 29, thus

    1. R−B7 ch   **B** x R
    2. N−K7 mate

If your solution is correct, check the following table for the approximate USCF rating at which you performed.

    1. Rb7-c7 +   **B**d6xc7
    2. Nd5-e7 mate

Table for Mate-Rater 35

time (sec)	rating	low	high	time (sec)	rating	low	high
5	2374	2174	2592	310	1424	1304	1555
10	2179	1995	2379	320	1419	1299	1549
20	2000	1831	2183	330	1413	1294	1543
30	1902	1742	2076	340	1408	1289	1537
40	1835	1681	2003	350	1403	1285	1532
50	1785	1635	1949	360	1398	1280	1526
60	1745	1598	1905	370	1393	1276	1521
70	1712	1568	1869	380	1389	1272	1516
80	1684	1543	1839	390	1384	1268	1511
90	1660	1520	1812	400	1380	1264	1507
100	1638	1500	1789	410	1376	1260	1502
110	1619	1483	1768	420	1372	1256	1497
120	1602	1467	1749	430	1368	1253	1493
130	1586	1453	1731	440	1364	1249	1489
140	1571	1439	1716	450	1360	1245	1485
150	1558	1427	1701	460	1356	1242	1481
160	1546	1416	1688	470	1353	1239	1477
170	1534	1405	1675	480	1349	1236	1473
180	1523	1395	1663	490	1346	1232	1469
190	1513	1386	1652	500	1342	1229	1465
200	1504	1377	1642	510	1339	1226	1462
210	1495	1369	1632	520	1336	1223	1458
220	1486	1361	1622	530	1333	1220	1455
230	1478	1353	1613	540	1330	1218	1452
240	1470	1346	1605	550	1327	1215	1448
250	1463	1340	1597	560	1324	1212	1445
260	1456	1333	1589	570	1321	1210	1442
270	1449	1327	1582	580	1318	1207	1439
280	1442	1321	1575	590	1315	1204	1436
290	1436	1315	1568	600	1312	1202	1433
300	1430	1310	1561				

Problem 36

(a) WHITE to move and win in two.
(b) If it were BLACK's move instead of WHITE's,
    give his best move.

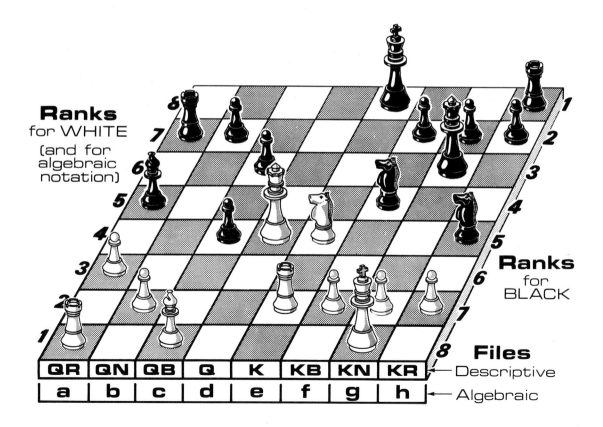

Answers to Problem 36

(a)   1.N−KB6 dbl ch   **K−KB1**   1. Ne4-f6 + +   **Ke8-f8**
            2.R−K8 mate   2. Re2-e8 mate

(b)   1. . . .   **Q** x P mate   1. . . .   **Q**g6xg2 mate

Problem 37

WHITE to move and win in two.

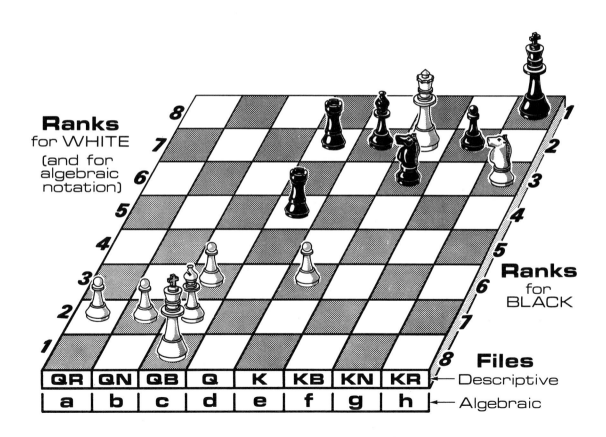

1.Q—N8 ch   **N x Q**   1. Qf7-g8 +   **Nf6xg8**
2.N—B7 mate   2. Nh6-f7 mate

Warm-Up Problem 38

(a) WHITE to move and win in two.
(b) If it were BLACK's move, give his best move(s).

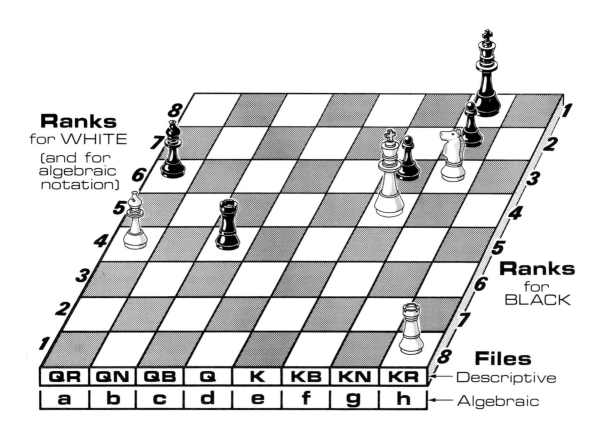

Answers to Problem 38

(a)

1.R−KR8 ch	**K−B2**	1. Rh1-h8 +	**Kg8-f7**
2.B−K8 mate		2. Ba4-e8 mate	
or		*or*	
2.R−KB8 mate		2. Rh8-f8 mate	

All tested players with ratings between 1180 and 2000 answered (a) correctly.

(b)

1. . . .	**B−QB1** ch	1. . . .	**Ba6-c8** +
2.B−Q7	**B** x B mate	2. Ba4-d7	**B**c8xd7 mate

Warm-Up Problem 39

Insert a sheet of paper behind this page to conceal Mate-Rater
Problem 40, which follows.

WHITE to move and win in two.

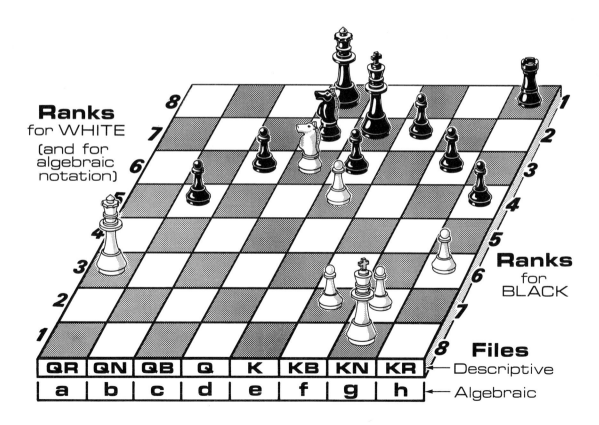

Answer to Problem 39

1. N−KB5 dbl ch	**K−K1**
2. N−KN7 mate	

Only a double check defeats BLACK in two. For example, if the White Knight is moved 1. N−K4, then 1. . . . **P−QB4** saves the day for BLACK.*Only two tested players — one rated 1556 and the other close to 2000 — missed this.

1. Nd6-f5 + +	**Ke7-e8**
2. Nf5-g7 mate	

*If 1. Nd6-e4, then 1. . . . . c6-c5 saves the day.

Mate-Rater Problem 40

WHITE to move and win in two.

1. _____ _____
2. _____ mate Time required:

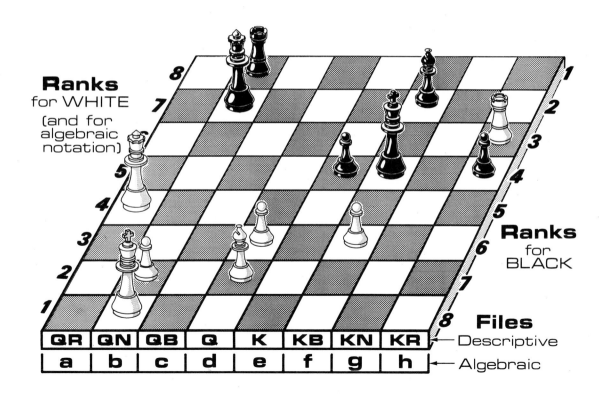

Ranks
for WHITE
(and for
algebraic
notation)

Ranks
for
BLACK

Files

QR	QN	QB	Q	K	KB	KN	KR

— Descriptive

a	b	c	d	e	f	g	h

— Algebraic

Answer to Problem 40

1.Q−K4 ch   **Q** x Q

2.QP x **Q** mate

All of the Black King's next-move squares are controlled by WHITE's Rook, Bishop Pawn, and Bishop. Moving 1.Q−K4 ch is the first step toward administering a fatal check to the Black King, this task eventually falling to WHITE's Queen Pawn when it captures the Black Queen.

About one player in eight failed to solve this in 10 minutes, and their ratings ranged from 1286 to slightly below 2000. If you solved it correctly in 10 minutes or less, use the following table to determine the approximate USCF rating at which you performed.

1. Qa4-e4 +   **Q**b7xe4
2. d3xe4 mate

time (sec)	rating	low	high	time (sec)	rating	low	high
5	2143	1975	2325	310	1428	1316	1549
10	2002	1845	2171	320	1423	1312	1544
20	1870	1724	2028	330	1419	1308	1539
30	1797	1656	1949	340	1415	1304	1535
40	1746	1610	1894	350	1411	1301	1530
50	1709	1575	1853	360	1407	1297	1526
60	1678	1547	1820	370	1403	1293	1522
70	1653	1524	1793	380	1399	1290	1518
80	1631	1504	1770	390	1396	1287	1514
90	1613	1486	1749	400	1392	1284	1510
100	1596	1471	1731	410	1389	1280	1507
110	1581	1457	1715	420	1386	1277	1503
120	1568	1445	1700	430	1383	1274	1500
130	1555	1434	1687	440	1379	1272	1496
140	1544	1423	1675	450	1376	1269	1493
150	1533	1414	1663	460	1373	1266	1490
160	1524	1405	1653	470	1370	1263	1487
170	1515	1396	1643	480	1368	1261	1484
180	1506	1388	1634	490	1365	1258	1481
190	1498	1381	1625	500	1362	1256	1478
200	1491	1374	1617	510	1359	1253	1475
210	1484	1368	1609	520	1357	1251	1472
220	1477	1361	1602	530	1354	1248	1469
230	1470	1355	1595	540	1352	1246	1466
240	1464	1350	1588	550	1349	1244	1464
250	1458	1344	1582	560	1347	1242	1461
260	1453	1339	1576	570	1345	1240	1459
270	1447	1334	1570	580	1342	1237	1456
280	1442	1329	1564	590	1340	1235	1454
290	1437	1325	1559	600	1338	1233	1451
300	1432	1320	1554				

Problem 41

WHITE to move and win in two.

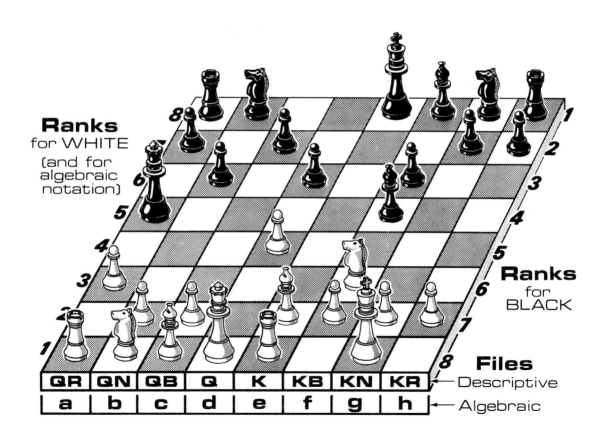

Ranks
for WHITE
(and for
algebraic
notation)

Ranks
for
BLACK

Files

| QR | QN | QB | Q | K | KB | KN | KR | ← Descriptive |
| a | b | c | d | e | f | g | h | ← Algebraic |

111

1.B—QN5 dbl ch	**K—KB2**	1. Be2-b5 ++	**Ke8-f7**
2.B—K8 mate		2. Bb5-e8 mate	
or		*or*	
1.B—QN5 dbl ch	**K—Q1**	1. Be2-b5 ++	**Ke8-d8**
2.R—K8 mate		2. Re1-e8 mate	

Problem 42

WHITE to move and win in two.

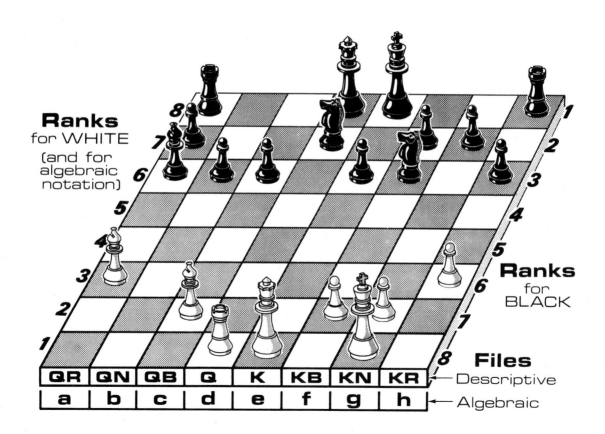

Answer to Problem 42

1.Q x **P** ch	**P** x Q	1. Qe1xe6 +	f7xe6
2.B—N6 mate		2. Bc2-g6 mate	
or			
1.Q x **P** ch	**Q—K2**	1. Qe1xe6 +	**Q**d8-e7
2.Q x **Q** mate		2. Qe6xe7 mate.	

Warm-Up Problem 43

WHITE to move and win in two.

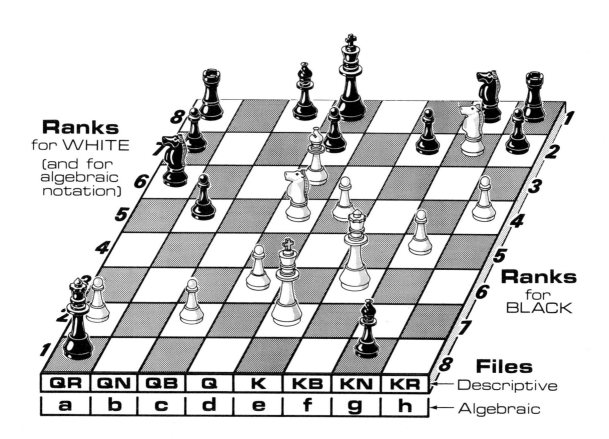

Ranks for WHITE (and for algebraic notation)

Ranks for BLACK

Files

QR	QN	QB	Q	K	KB	KN	KR	← Descriptive
a	b	c	d	e	f	g	h	← Algebraic

115

Answer to Problem 43

1.Q—KB6 ch!	N x Q	

2.B—K7 mate

1. Qf3-f6 +!   Ng8xf6
2. Bd6-e7 mate

Problem 43 probably looks familiar because it represents the board as it appeared during a famous game played in London in 1851. The great master, Adolf Anderssen, played WHITE so brilliantly that this game is affectionately known as the 'Immortal Game.' Anderssen, seeing the board as illustrated in Problem 43, realized that the Black King had no available next-move squares so that B—K7 would produce mate, provided the power of BLACK's King's Knight could first be removed from this square. His move 1.Q—KB6 ch does this nicely. BLACK has no move other than N x Q. With the shadow of BLACK's Knight now removed from the square, the White Bishop knifes the Black King with 2.B—K7 mate.

All tested players with ratings above 1200 solved this correctly. Of course Anderssen had recognized the mate at a much earlier stage than portrayed here.

Warm-Up Problem 44

Insert a sheet of paper behind this page to cover Mate-Rater Problem 45.

(a) WHITE to move and win in two.
(b) If it were BLACK's move, give his best move(s).

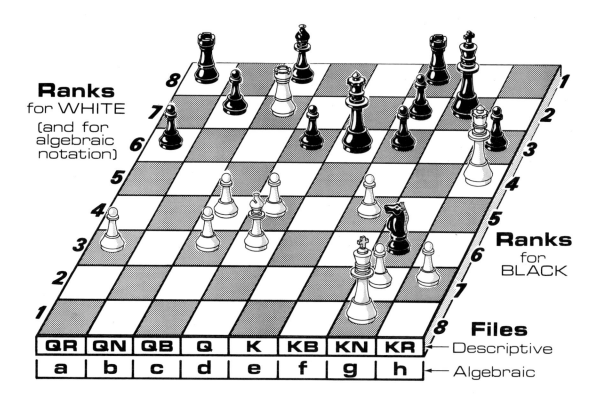

Answers to Problem 44

(a)

| 1.Q−KN6 ch | **K−R1** | 1. Qh5-g6 + | **Kg7-h8** |
| 2.Q−R7 mate | | 2. Qg6-h7 mate | |

All the pretested, rated players solved this problem easily.

(b)

| 1. . . . | **Q−K8** ch | 1. . . . | **Qe6-e1** |
| 2.B−KB1 | **Q** x B mate | 2. Bd3-f1 | **Qe1xf1** mate |

Mate-Rater Problem 45

WHITE to move and win in two.

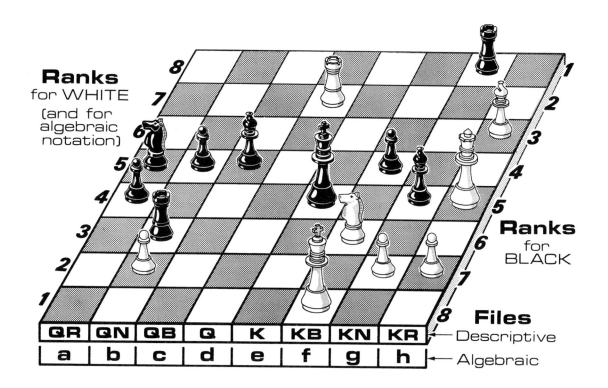

Ranks
for WHITE
(and for
algebraic
notation)

Ranks
for
BLACK

Files

QR	QN	QB	Q	K	KB	KN	KR	— Descriptive
a	b	c	d	e	f	g	h	— Algebraic

119

Answer to Problem 45

1.Q−K7 ch	**B** x Q
2.R−Q4 mate	

In problem 45, a systematic study of the Black King's next-move squares shows that all are denied him by WHITE's Knight, Bishop, and Rook. WHITE's first check. 1.Q−K7 ch then forces 1.... **B** x Q, which permits the White Rook to administer the *coup de grace* with 2.R−Q4 mate. About 40% of the rated players were unable to solve this problem in 10 minutes. The highest rating that missed was 1733 but almost all the rest that missed were below 1570. One player, rated 1717, solved it in 10 seconds! He would have a rating in the 1832−2180 range, showing that on this problem he performed much above his present 1717 rating. If your solution was correct and achieved in 10 minutes or less, check your performance by using the following table.

1. Qh4-e7+	**B**c5xe7
2 Rd7-d4 mate	

time (sec)	rating	low	high	time (sec)	rating	low	high
5	2128	1951	2322	310	1463	1341	1596
10	1998	1832	2180	320	1459	1337	1592
20	1877	1720	2047	330	1455	1333	1587
30	1809	1658	1973	340	1451	1330	1583
40	1762	1615	1923	350	1447	1326	1579
50	1727	1583	1884	360	1443	1323	1575
60	1698	1557	1853	370	1440	1320	1571
70	1675	1535	1827	380	1436	1316	1567
80	1655	1517	1805	390	1433	1313	1564
90	1637	1500	1786	400	1430	1310	1560
100	1621	1486	1769	410	1427	1307	1556
110	1607	1473	1754	420	1423	1305	1553
120	1595	1462	1740	430	1420	1302	1550
130	1583	1451	1728	440	1417	1299	1547
140	1573	1441	1716	450	1415	1296	1543
150	1563	1432	1705	460	1412	1294	1540
160	1554	1424	1695	470	1409	1291	1537
170	1545	1416	1686	480	1406	1289	1534
180	1537	1409	1677	490	1404	1286	1531
190	1530	1402	1669	500	1401	1284	1529
200	1523	1395	1661	510	1399	1282	1526
210	1516	1389	1654	520	1396	1279	1523
220	1509	1383	1647	530	1394	1277	1521
230	1503	1378	1640	540	1391	1275	1518
240	1498	1373	1634	550	1389	1273	1516
250	1492	1367	1628	560	1387	1271	1513
260	1487	1363	1622	570	1384	1269	1511
270	1482	1358	1617	580	1382	1267	1508
280	1477	1353	1611	590	1380	1265	1506
290	1472	1349	1606	600	1378	1263	1504
300	1468	1345	1601				

Problem 46

WHITE to move and win in two.

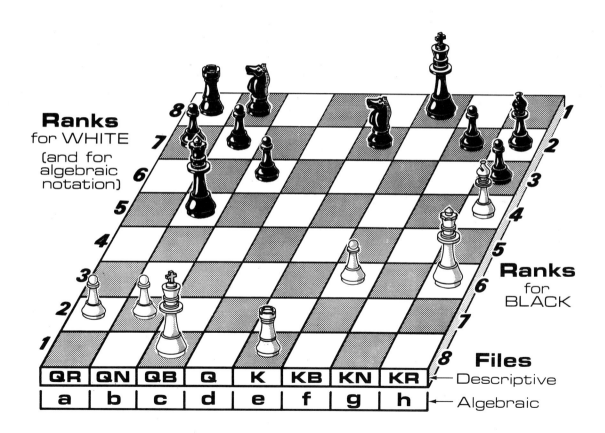

Ranks
for WHITE
(and for
algebraic
notation)

Ranks
for
BLACK

QR	QN	QB	Q	K	KB	KN	KR	← Descriptive
a	b	c	d	e	f	g	h	← Algebraic

Files

121

Answer to Problem 46

1. Q−QB8 ch   N x Q   1. Qh3-c8 +   Ne7xc8
2. R−K8 mate   2. Re1-e8 mate

Problem 47

(a) WHITE to move and win in two.
(b) If it were BLACK's move instead of WHITE's,
give his best move(s).

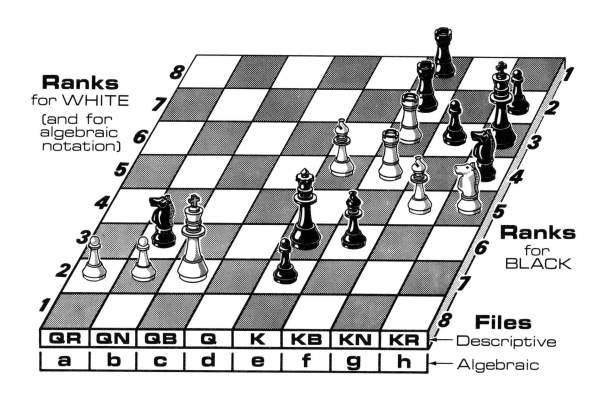

Answers to Problem 47

(a)   1.R x N ch   **B – KN2**   1. Rf5xh5 +   **K**h6-g7
             2.R x **NP** mate   2. Rf6xg6 mate

The Black King succumbs to a double check by the White Rook and Bishop.

(b)   1. . . .   **B – K5** mate   1. . . .   **B**f3-e4 mate

Problem 48

WHITE to move and win in two.

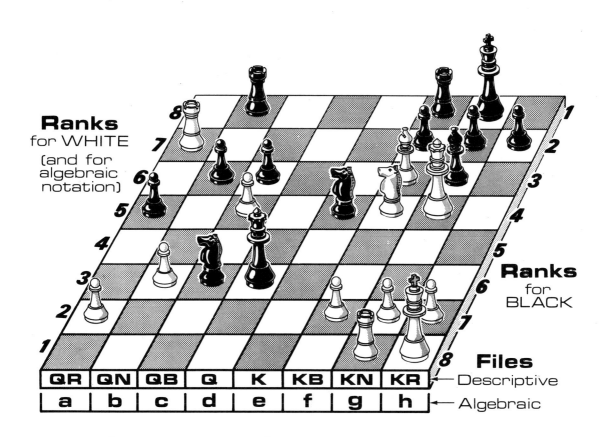

Answer to Problem 48

1.Q−KR6   **P** x Q
2.N x **P** (or N-K7) mate*
or
1.Q−KR6   **P** x B
2.Q−KN7 mate
or
1.Q−KR6   **Q** x N
2.Q x **P** mate

1. Qg5-h6   g7xh6
2. Nf5xh6 (or Nf5-e7) mate**

1. Qg5-h6   g7xf6
2. Qh6-g7 mate

1. Qg5-h6   **Q**d3xf5
2. Qh6xg7 mate

Warm-Up Problem 49

Place a sheet of paper behind this page to cover Mate-Rater Problem 50.

WHITE to move and win in two.

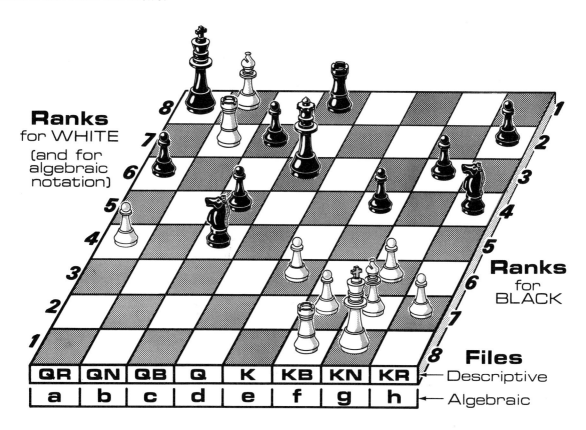

Ranks for WHITE (and for algebraic notation)

Ranks for BLACK

Files

QR	QN	QB	Q	K	KB	KN	KR	— Descriptive
a	b	c	d	e	f	g	h	— Algebraic

Answer to Problem 49

1. R—R7 dbl ck   **K** x B
2. R—R8 mate

Most of the tested players solved this in less than a minute. However, four of them (ratings: 1286, 1444, 1496, and 1682) missed it.

1. Rb7-a7 + +   **K**a8xb8
2. Ra7-a8 mate

Mate-Rater Problem 50

BLACK to move and win in two.

1. . . . _____
2. _____ _____

Time required:

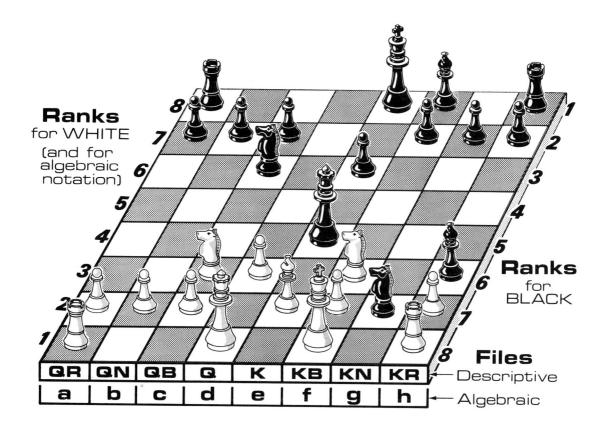

Ranks
for WHITE
(and for
algebraic
notation)

Ranks
for
BLACK

Files

QR	QN	QB	Q	K	KB	KN	KR	← Descriptive
a	b	c	d	e	f	g	h	← Algebraic

129

Answer to Problem 50

1. . . . **N−KR5** dis ch
2. K−K1 **N** x N mate
or
2. K−KN1 **Q−KN5** mate

Of the tested players, five (ratings: 1180, 1239, 1536, 1886, and 1932) missed this problem. If your solution was correct, use the following table to determine the approximate USCF rating at which you performed.

1. . . . Ng2-h4 +
2. Kt1-e1 Nh4xf3 mate
or
2. Kf1-g1 Qe4-g4 mate

Table for Mate-Rater 50

time (sec)	rating	low	high	time (sec)	rating	low	high
5	2300	2098	2520	310	1460	1332	1600
10	2131	1944	2335	320	1455	1327	1594
20	1974	1801	2163	330	1450	1323	1589
30	1888	1723	2069	340	1445	1319	1584
40	1829	1669	2004	350	1441	1314	1579
50	1785	1629	1956	360	1436	1310	1574
60	1749	1596	1917	370	1432	1306	1569
70	1720	1569	1885	380	1428	1303	1564
80	1695	1546	1857	390	1423	1299	1560
90	1673	1526	1833	400	1419	1295	1555
100	1654	1509	1812	410	1416	1292	1551
110	1636	1493	1793	420	1412	1288	1547
120	1621	1479	1776	430	1408	1285	1543
130	1606	1466	1760	440	1405	1282	1539
140	1593	1454	1746	450	1401	1279	1535
150	1581	1443	1733	460	1398	1275	1532
160	1570	1433	1721	470	1394	1272	1528
170	1560	1423	1709	480	1391	1269	1525
180	1550	1414	1698	490	1388	1267	1521
190	1541	1406	1688	500	1385	1264	1518
200	1532	1398	1679	510	1382	1261	1514
210	1524	1390	1670	520	1379	1258	1511
220	1516	1383	1661	530	1376	1256	1508
230	1509	1377	1653	540	1373	1253	1505
240	1502	1370	1645	550	1371	1251	1502
250	1495	1364	1638	560	1368	1248	1499
260	1488	1358	1631	570	1365	1246	1496
270	1482	1353	1624	580	1363	1243	1493
280	1476	1347	1618	590	1360	1241	1490
290	1471	1342	1612	600	1357	1239	1488
300	1465	1337	1606				

Problem 51

WHITE to move and win in two.

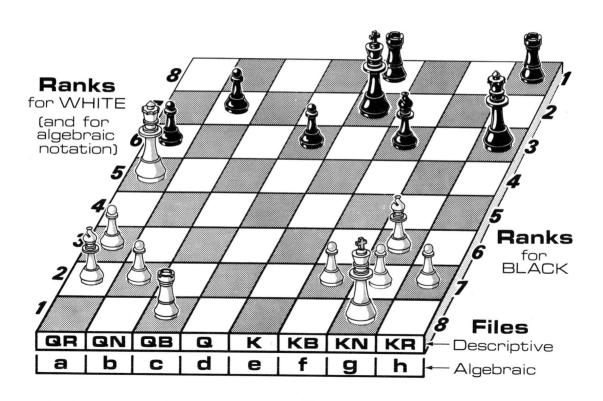

Ranks for WHITE (and for algebraic notation)

Ranks for BLACK

Files

QR	QN	QB	Q	K	KB	KN	KR	← Descriptive
a	b	c	d	e	f	g	h	← Algebraic

131

Answer to Problem 51

Each move of WHITE must be a check of the Black King or else BLACK will move 1. . . . **Q** x R ch* which will result in mate of the White King. Thus,

1.B x **P** ch	**K** x B (or **K − Q2**)
2.Q−QB7 mate	
or	
1.Q−QB7 ch	**K − KB1**
2.Q−KB7 mate	

1. . . .	**Q**h6xc1 +
1. Bg3xd6 +	**K**e7xd6 (or **K**e7-d7)
2. Qa5-c7 mate	
1. Qa5-c7 +	**K**e7-f8
2. Qc7-f7 mate	

Problem 52

(a) WHITE to move and win in two.
(b) If it were BLACK's move instead of WHITE's,
    give his best move(s).

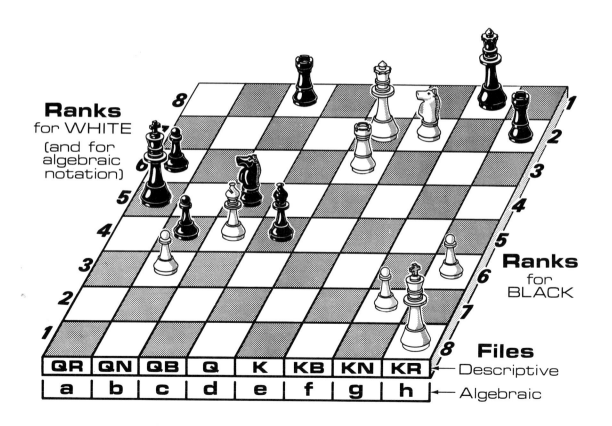

Answers to Problem 52

(a) 1. Q x **N** ch   (**B** or **R**) x Q   1. Qe7xc5 +   (**B**d4 or **R**c8)xc5
     2. R x **P** mate   2. Re6xa6 mate

(b) 1. . . .   **R** x P ch   1. . . .   **R**h7xh3 +
     2. P x **R**   **Q–KN8** mate   2. g2xh3   **Q**g8-g1 mate

Warm-Up Problem 53

WHITE to move and win in two.

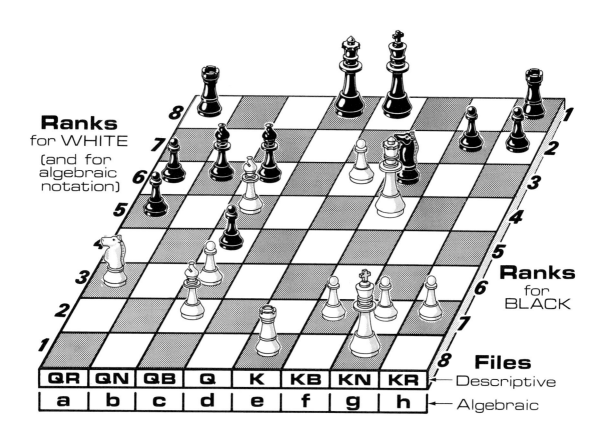

Ranks for WHITE (and for algebraic notation)

Ranks for BLACK

Files

QR	QN	QB	Q	K	KB	KN	KR	← Descriptive
----	----	----	---	---	----	----	----	
a	b	c	d	e	f	g	h	← Algebraic

135

Answer to Problem 53

1.Q−KN6 ch	P x Q	1. Qf5-g6 +	h7xg6
2.B x P mate		2. Bc2xg6 mate	

All of the Black King's next-move squares are denied him and only the square he occupied was safe until the White Queen's suicidal attack permitted the White Bishop to perform the *coup de grace.* Many players solved this in less than 30 seconds and only one (rating: 1180) missed it.

Warm-Up Problem 54

Insert a sheet of paper behind this page to cover Mate-Rater
Problem 55.

WHITE to move and win in two.

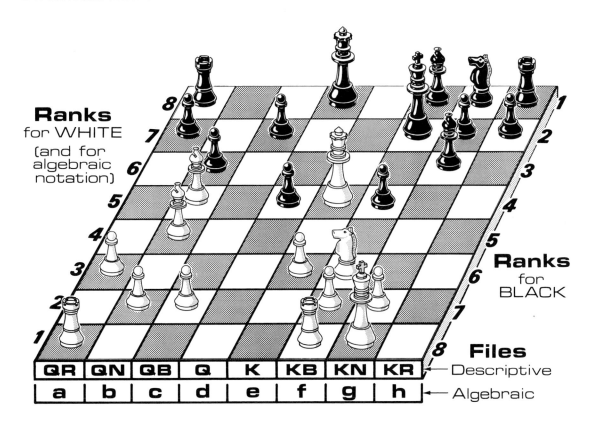

137

Answer to Problem 54

1.B−K8 ch	**Q** x B	1. Bb5-e8 +	**Q**d8xe8
2.N−KN5 mate		2. Nf3-g5 mate	

Of the 43 tested players, four (ratings: 1180, 1399, 1444, and 1682) missed this.

Mate-Rater Problem 55

WHITE to move and win in two.

1. _____ _____
2. _____ mate Time required:

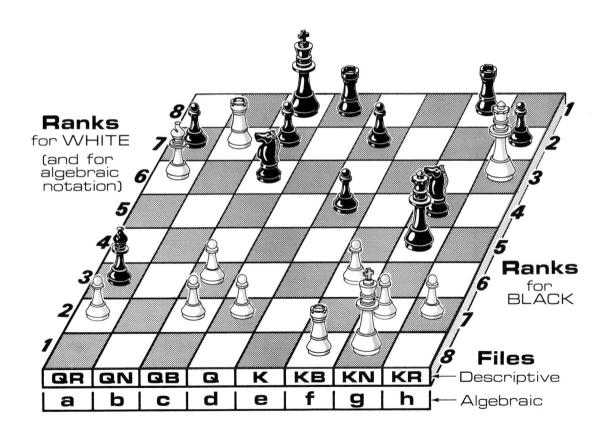

Ranks
for WHITE
(and for
algebraic
notation)

Ranks
for
BLACK

Files

QR	QN	QB	Q	K	KB	KN	KR	— Descriptive
a	b	c	d	e	f	g	h	— Algebraic

139

Answer to Problem 55

1. R – QN6 dis ch   **K – Q2**
2. Q x **N** (QB6) mate

Of the tested players one out of five missed this, their ratings being 1180, 1239, 1496, 1536, 1550, 1598, 1805, and 1809. If you solved it correctly within ten minutes, check the approximate USCF rating at which you performed by using the following table.

1. Rb7-b6 +   **K**c8-d7
2. Qh6xc6 mate

Table for Mate-Rater 55

time (sec)	rating	low	high	time (sec)	rating	low	high
5	2156	1978	2350	310	1493	1370	1628
10	2027	1860	2210	320	1489	1366	1623
20	1906	1748	2078	330	1485	1362	1619
30	1838	1686	2004	340	1481	1359	1615
40	1792	1644	1953	350	1477	1355	1610
50	1757	1611	1915	360	1474	1352	1606
60	1728	1585	1884	370	1470	1349	1603
70	1705	1564	1858	380	1467	1345	1599
80	1685	1545	1836	390	1463	1342	1595
90	1667	1529	1817	400	1460	1339	1591
100	1652	1515	1800	410	1457	1336	1588
110	1638	1502	1785	420	1454	1333	1585
120	1625	1491	1771	430	1451	1331	1581
130	1613	1480	1759	440	1448	1328	1578
140	1603	1470	1747	450	1445	1325	1575
150	1593	1461	1737	460	1442	1323	1572
160	1584	1453	1727	470	1439	1320	1569
170	1575	1445	1717	480	1436	1318	1566
180	1567	1438	1709	490	1434	1315	1563
190	1560	1431	1700	500	1431	1313	1560
200	1553	1424	1693	510	1429	1311	1557
210	1546	1418	1685	520	1426	1308	1555
220	1540	1412	1678	530	1424	1306	1552
230	1534	1407	1672	540	1421	1304	1550
240	1528	1401	1665	550	1419	1302	1547
250	1522	1396	1659	560	1417	1300	1545
260	1517	1392	1654	570	1415	1298	1542
270	1512	1387	1648	580	1412	1296	1540
280	1507	1382	1643	590	1410	1294	1537
290	1502	1378	1638	600	1408	1292	1535
300	1498	1374	1633				

Problem 56

WHITE to move and win in two.

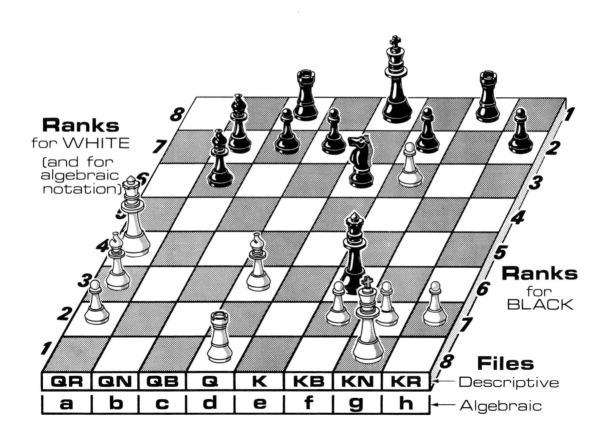

| QR | QN | QB | Q | K | KB | KN | KR | ← Descriptive |
| a | b | c | d | e | f | g | h | ← Algebraic |

141

Answer to Problem 56

1.Q x **P** ch   **K** x Q
2.B−QN5 mate
(by a deadly double check)

1. Qa4xd7 +   **K**e8xd7
2. Bd3-b5 mate

Problem 57

WHITE to move and win in two.

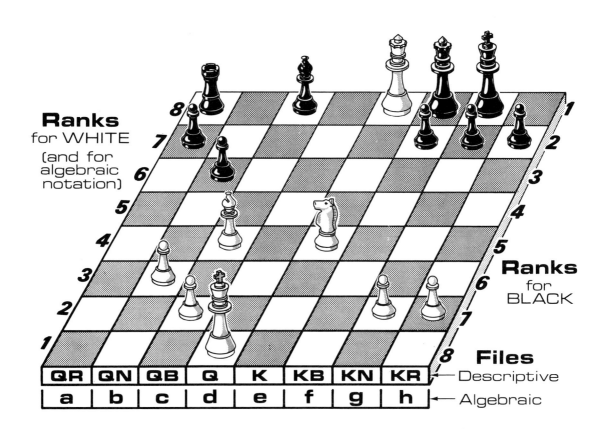

Files							
QR	QN	QB	Q	K	KB	KN	KR
a	b	c	d	e	f	g	h

Descriptive

Algebraic

143

Answer to Problem 57

1.B x **P** ch   **K − R1**

2.Q x **Q** mate

1. Bc4xf7 +   **K**g8-h8

2. Qe8xf8 mate

Problem 58

WHITE to move and mate in two.

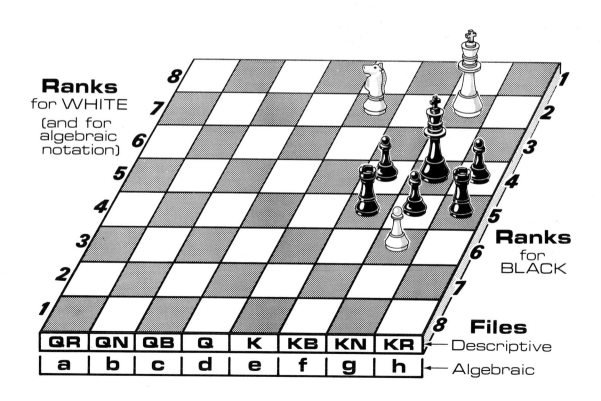

Ranks for WHITE (and for algebraic notation)

Ranks for BLACK

Files

QR	QN	QB	Q	K	KB	KN	KR	← Descriptive
a	b	c	d	e	f	g	h	← Algebraic

145

Answer to Problem 58

       1.N−N6!!   **R**−any safe square
BLACK can only move one Rook to safety whereupon
the White Pawn captures the other Rook and
checkmates the Black King. Thus,
           2.P x **R** mate
Most of the rated players solved this in about 2
minutes or less. Three of them (ratings: 1180, 1536,
and 1556) missed it. After WHITE moves 1.N−N6!,
BLACK is in *zugzwang* — that is, his situation is one
in which he is limited to moves that bring damage to
himself.

1. Ne7-g6!!   **R** (f4 or h4)—any safe square

2. g3x(f4 or h4) mate

Problem 59

WHITE to move and win in two.

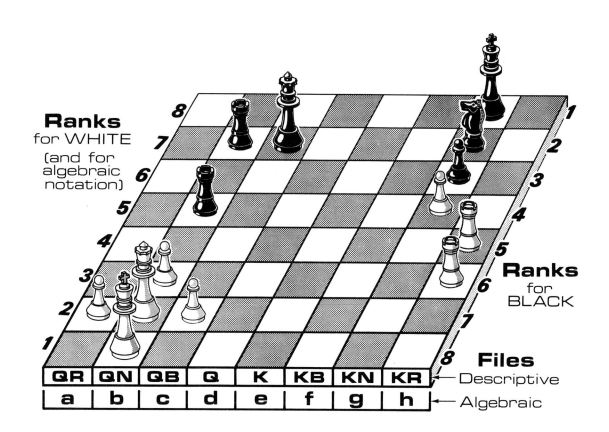

Files								
QR	**QN**	**QB**	**Q**	**K**	**KB**	**KN**	**KR**	← Descriptive
a	**b**	**c**	**d**	**e**	**f**	**g**	**h**	← Algebraic

147

Answer to Problem 59

| 1. R−R8 ch | **K−B2** | 1. Rh4-h8 + | **Kg8-f7** |
| 2. Q−KB6 mate | | 2. Qb2-f6 mate | |

Problem 60

WHITE to move and win in two.

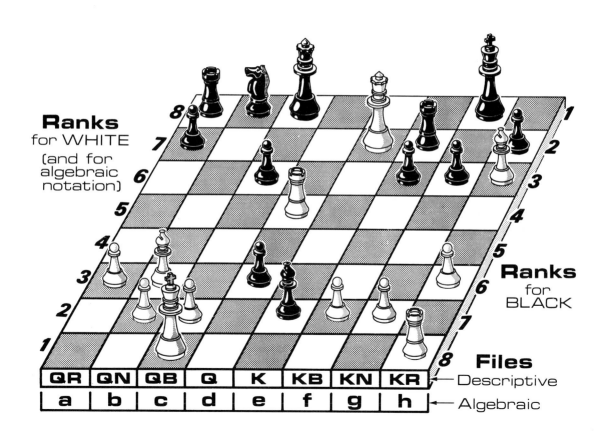

QR	QN	QB	Q	K	KB	KN	KR	← Descriptive
a	b	c	d	e	f	g	h	← Algebraic

Files

149

Answer to Problem 60

1.R—Q8 ch   **Q** x R

2.Q x **Q** mate

1. Rd5-d8 +   **Q**c8xd8

2. Qe7xd8 mate

8. Three-Move Problems

Because they involve three moves, the problems in this section generally seemed to present much more difficulty for the low-rated, less experienced players. Often they could not solve these problems in 10 minutes. The more experienced players, on the other hand, seemed to take them in stride, often finding them less difficult than some of the preceding two-move problems. The mate-rater problems are numbered 62, 65, 70, 75, 80, and 85.

Warm-Up Problem 61

Insert a sheet of paper behind this page to cover Mate-Rater Problem 62.

WHITE to move and win in three.

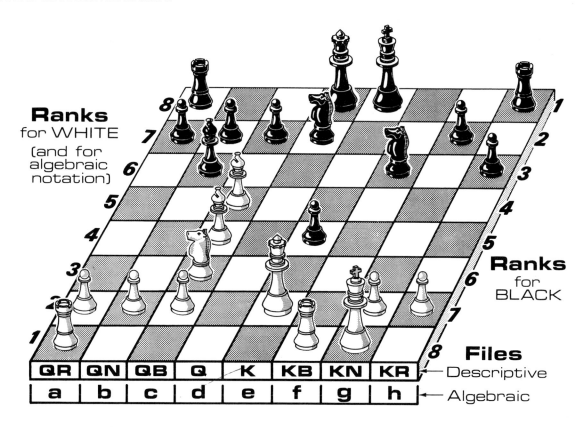

Ranks
for WHITE
(and for algebraic notation)

Ranks
for BLACK

Files
— Descriptive
— Algebraic

| QR | QN | QB | Q | K | KB | KN | KR |
| a | b | c | d | e | f | g | h |

153

Answer to Problem 61

1.Q x P ch	**N–K4***	1. Qe2xe4 +	Nd7-e5
2.Q x N ch	**Q–K2**	2. Qe4xe5 +	Qd8-e7
3.Q x **Q** mate		3. Qe5xe7 mate	

or

1.Q x P ch	**N–K4**	1. Qe2xe4 +	Nd7-e5
2.Q x N ch	**K–Q2**	2. Qe4xe5 +	Ke8-d7
3.Q–K6 mate		3. Qe5-e6 mate	

*If, instead, 1. . . . **N** x Q, then 2. **B–KB7** mate.

Mate-Rater Problem 62

WHITE to move and win in three.

1. _____ _____
2. _____ _____
3. _____ mate Time required:

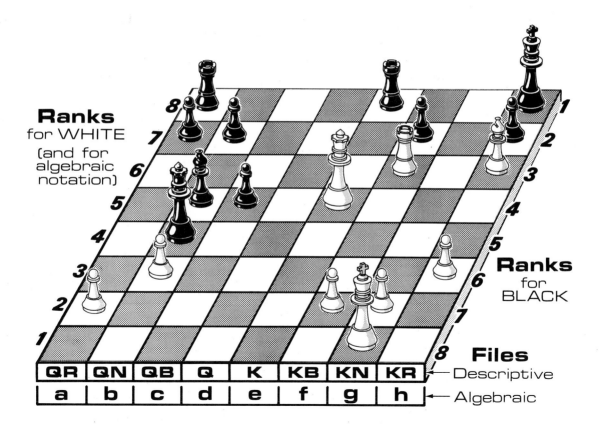

Ranks
for WHITE
(and for
algebraic
notation)

Ranks
for
BLACK

Files

| QR | QN | QB | Q | K | KB | KN | KR | ← Descriptive |

| a | b | c | d | e | f | g | h | ← Algebraic |

155

Answer to Problem 62

1. R−K6 dis ch   **P−KB3**
2. Q x P ch   **K−N1**
3. Q−N7 mate

Many solved this in less than two minutes but it stumped three of the tested players (ratings: 1364, 1443, and 1555). If you solved it correctly within 10 minutes, check the approximate USCF rating at which you performed, by using the following table.

1. Rf6-e6 +   f7-f6
2. Qe5xf6 +   **K**h8-g8
3. Qf6-g7 mate

Table for Mate-Rater 62

time (sec)	rating	low	high	time (sec)	rating	low	high
5	2623	2417	2846	310	1349	1243	1464
10	2346	2162	2545	320	1342	1237	1456
20	2098	1933	2276	330	1335	1231	1449
30	1965	1811	2132	340	1329	1225	1442
40	1876	1729	2036	350	1323	1219	1435
50	1810	1668	1964	360	1317	1213	1429
60	1758	1620	1907	370	1311	1208	1422
70	1714	1580	1860	380	1305	1203	1416
80	1678	1546	1821	390	1300	1198	1410
90	1646	1517	1786	400	1295	1193	1405
100	1619	1492	1756	410	1289	1188	1399
110	1594	1469	1729	420	1284	1184	1394
120	1572	1449	1705	430	1280	1179	1388
130	1552	1430	1684	440	1275	1175	1383
140	1533	1413	1664	450	1270	1171	1378
150	1516	1397	1645	460	1266	1166	1373
160	1501	1383	1628	470	1261	1162	1369
170	1486	1369	1612	480	1257	1158	1364
180	1472	1357	1598	490	1253	1155	1359
190	1460	1345	1584	500	1249	1151	1355
200	1448	1334	1571	510	1245	1147	1351
210	1436	1324	1558	520	1241	1144	1346
220	1426	1314	1547	530	1237	1140	1342
230	1415	1304	1536	540	1233	1137	1338
240	1406	1295	1525	550	1230	1133	1334
250	1396	1287	1515	560	1226	1130	1330
260	1388	1279	1506	570	1223	1127	1327
270	1379	1271	1496	580	1219	1124	1323
280	1371	1264	1488	590	1216	1121	1319
290	1363	1256	1479	600	1213	1118	1316
300	1356	1250	1471				

Problem 63

WHITE to move and win in three.

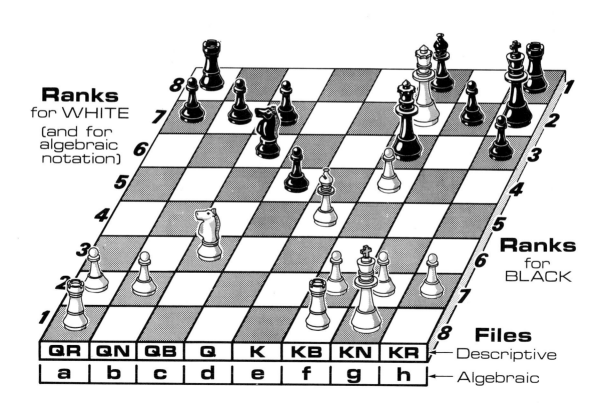

| QR | QN | QB | Q | K | KB | KN | KR | ← Descriptive |
| a | b | c | d | e | f | g | h | ← Algebraic |

157

Answer to Problem 63

1.Q−KN6 ch	**Q** x Q
2.P x **Q** ch	**K−N1**
3.B x **P** mate	

or

1. Q-KN6 ch	**K-N1**
2. B x P ch	**Q-K3**(or B2)
3. B x Q mate	

1. Qf7-g6 +	**Q**f6xg6
2. f5xg6 +	**K**h7-g8
3. Be4xd5 mate	

1. Qf7-g6 +	**K**h7-g8
2. Be5xd5 +	**Q**f6-e6 (or f7)
3. Bd5xe6 (or f7) mate	

Warm-Up Problem 64

Place a sheet of paper behind this page to conceal Mate-Rater
Problem 65, which follows.

BLACK to move and win in three.

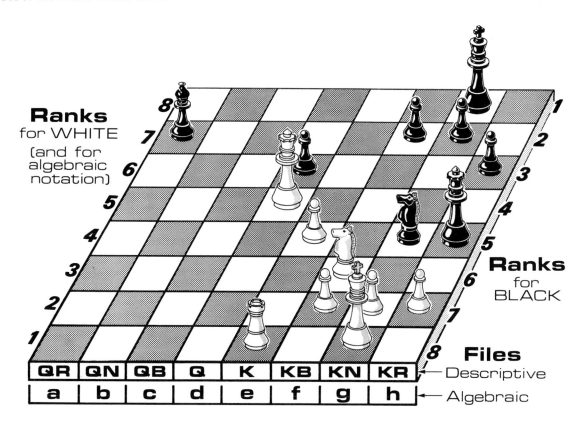

Ranks
for WHITE
(and for
algebraic
notation)

Ranks
for
BLACK

Files
— Descriptive

— Algebraic

QR	QN	QB	Q	K	KB	KN	KR
a	b	c	d	e	f	g	h

Answer to Problem 64

1. . . .	**Q** x BP ch
2. K−R1	**Q−N8** ch!
3. R *or* N x **Q**	**N−B7** mate

1. . . .	**Q**h4xf2 +
2. Kg1-h1	**Q**f2-g1 +!
3. (Rel or Nf3)xg1	Ng4-f2 mate

This is a recurrent theme. Smother the King on R1 with his own men, sacrificing your own to accomplish it, provided you have a Knight that can attack this corner square without reprisal.

Mate-Rater Problem 65

WHITE to move and win in three.

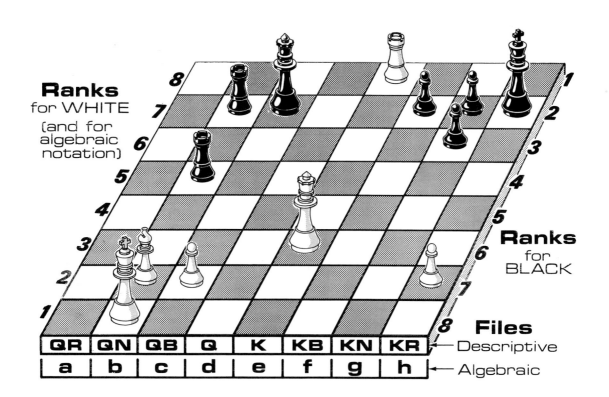

161

Answer to Problem 65

1. R−KR8 ch	**K x R**
2. Q−KR6 ch	**K−N1**
3. Q x **P** (on KN7) mate	

About one out of seven of the tested players missed this. Their ratings were 1180, 1216, 1399, 1444, 1556, and 1615. If your solution was correct, check the USCF rating at which you performed, by using the following table.

1. Re8-h8 +	**K**h7xh8
2. Qe3-h6 +	**K**h8-g8
3. Qh6xg7 mate	

Table for Mate-Rater 65

time (sec)	rating	low	high	time (sec)	rating	low	high
5	1932	1762	2119	310	1404	1280	1540
10	1831	1670	2009	320	1401	1277	1536
20	1736	1583	1904	330	1397	1274	1532
30	1682	1534	1845	340	1394	1271	1529
40	1645	1500	1804	350	1391	1268	1526
50	1617	1474	1773	360	1388	1266	1522
60	1594	1454	1749	370	1385	1263	1519
70	1575	1437	1728	380	1382	1260	1516
80	1559	1422	1710	390	1379	1258	1513
90	1545	1409	1695	400	1377	1255	1510
100	1533	1397	1681	410	1374	1253	1507
110	1521	1387	1668	420	1372	1251	1504
120	1511	1378	1657	430	1369	1248	1501
130	1502	1369	1647	440	1367	1246	1499
140	1493	1362	1638	450	1364	1244	1496
150	1485	1354	1629	460	1362	1242	1494
160	1478	1348	1621	470	1360	1240	1491
170	1471	1341	1613	480	1357	1238	1489
180	1464	1335	1606	490	1355	1236	1486
190	1458	1330	1599	500	1353	1234	1484
200	1453	1324	1593	510	1351	1232	1482
210	1447	1320	1587	520	1349	1230	1479
220	1442	1315	1581	530	1347	1228	1477
230	1437	1310	1576	540	1345	1227	1475
240	1432	1306	1571	550	1343	1225	1473
250	1428	1302	1566	560	1341	1223	1471
260	1423	1298	1561	570	1339	1221	1469
270	1419	1294	1556	580	1338	1220	1467
280	1415	1290	1552	590	1336	1218	1465
290	1411	1287	1548	600	1334	1217	1463
300	1408	1284	1544				

Problem 66

BLACK to move and mate in three.

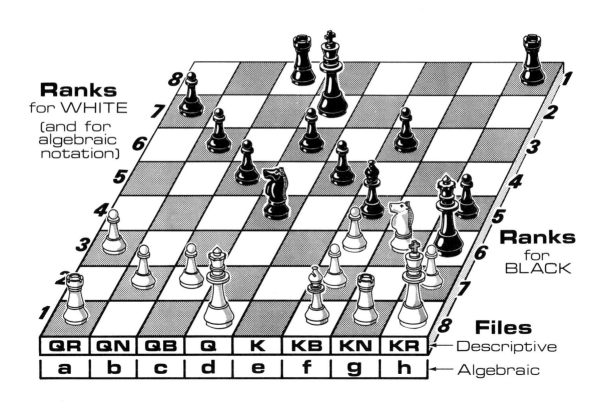

QR	QN	QB	Q	K	KB	KN	KR	← Descriptive
a	b	c	d	e	f	g	h	← Algebraic

Answer to Problem 66

1. . . .	**Q** x P ch	1. . . .	**Q**h3xh2 +
2.K x **Q**	**P** x N dbl ch	2. Kh1xh2	h4xg3 + +
3.K − KN2	**R − KR7** mate	3. Kh2-g2	**R**h8-h2 mate

Problem 67

BLACK to move and win in two or three.

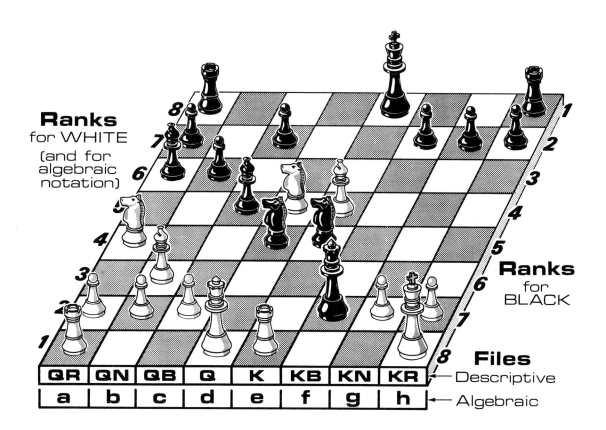

Answer to Problem 67

1. . . .	**Q–KN8** ch!	1. . . .	**Q**f2-g1 +!
2.K x **Q***	**N–KB6** dbl ch	2. Kh1xg1**	Nd4-f3 ++
3.K–R1	**N–KB7** mate	3. Kg1-h1	Ne4-f2 mate

*If 2. R x **Q,** then **N–KB7** mate.   **If 2. Re1xg1, then Ne4-f2 mate.

Warm-Up Problem 68

WHITE to move and win in three.

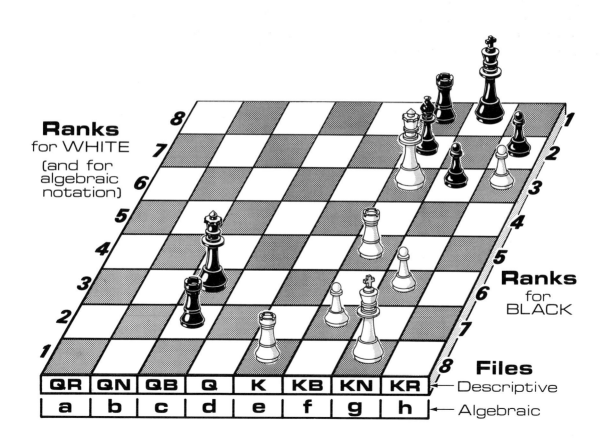

Ranks
for WHITE
(and for
algebraic
notation)

Ranks
for
BLACK

Files

QR	QN	QB	Q	K	KB	KN	KR	— Descriptive
a	b	c	d	e	f	g	h	— Algebraic

167

Answer to Problem 68

All the tested players found this solution readily, which is why it did not become a mate-rater.

1.Q x **B** ch!	**R** x Q
2.R−K8 ch	**R−B1**
3.R x **R** mate	

Either White Rook can be used to make the capture and achieve mate.

1.	Qf6xf7 +!	**Rf8xf7**
2.	Re1-e8+	**Rf7-f8**
3.	(Re8 or Rf4)xf8 mate	

Warm-Up Problem 69

Slip a sheet of paper behind this page to conceal Mate-Rater Problem 70.

WHITE to move and win in three.

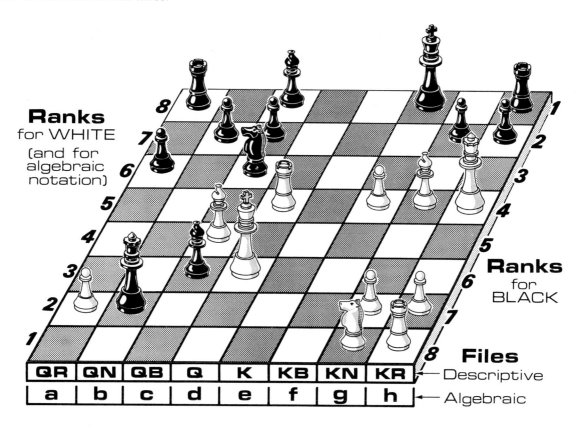

169

Answer to Problem 69

Over 80 years ago an internationally famous chessmaster perceived this combination to win. It employs the familiar theme of a Queen sacrifice that enables WHITE to subject the Black King to a devastating discovered check. Thus,

1.Q−B7 ch!	**K x Q**	1. Qh5-f7 +	**Kf8xf7**
2.R−Q8 dis ch	**B−K3**	2. Rd5-d8 +	**Bc8-e6**
3.B x **B** mate		3. Bc4xe6 mate	

Almost one out of five of the tested players missed this, their USCF ratings ranging from 1180 to 1809.

Mate-Rater Problem 70

WHITE to move and win in three (or four).

1. _____   _____
2. _____   _____
3. _____   _____
4. _____ mate Time required:

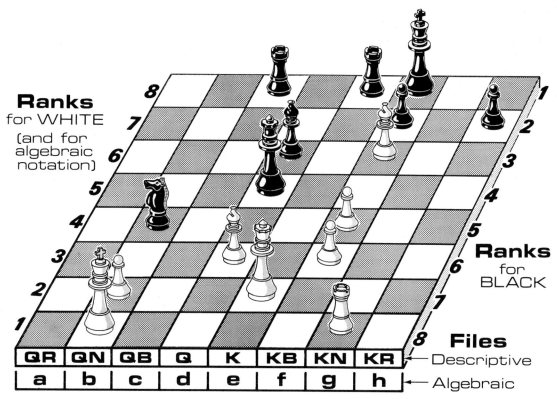

Ranks
for WHITE
(and for
algebraic
notation)

Ranks
for
BLACK

Files

QR	QN	QB	Q	K	KB	KN	KR	← Descriptive

a	b	c	d	e	f	g	h	← Algebraic

Answer to Problem 70

1. R–KN8 ch	K x R
2. Q–KN2 ch	**Q–KN4**
3. Q x **Q** ch	**K–B1**
4. Q–KN7 mate	

If the futile interposition of the Black Queen is omitted, this becomes a three-move mate, thus:

1. R–KN8 ch	**K x R**
2. Q–KN2 ch	**K–B1**
3. Q–KN7 mate	

About one out of seven of the tested players missed this; the USCF ratings for those who did not see the solution ranged from 1180 to 1886. If you solved it correctly in less than ten minutes, check the approximate USCF rating at which you performed, by using the following table.

1. Rg1-g8 +	Kf8xg8
2. Qe2-g2 +	Qd5-g5
3. Qg2xg5 +	Kg8-f8
4. Qg5-g7 mate	

Table for Mate-Rater 70

time (sec)	rating	low	high	time (sec)	rating	low	high
5	2084	1916	2266	310	1410	1296	1533
10	1952	1795	2122	320	1406	1292	1529
20	1828	1681	1987	330	1401	1289	1524
30	1759	1617	1913	340	1398	1285	1520
40	1711	1574	1861	350	1394	1282	1516
50	1676	1541	1822	360	1390	1278	1512
60	1647	1514	1791	370	1386	1275	1508
70	1623	1493	1765	380	1383	1272	1504
80	1603	1474	1743	390	1379	1268	1500
90	1585	1457	1724	400	1376	1265	1497
100	1569	1443	1707	410	1373	1262	1493
110	1555	1430	1691	420	1370	1260	1490
120	1542	1418	1677	430	1367	1257	1486
130	1531	1408	1665	440	1364	1254	1483
140	1520	1398	1653	450	1361	1251	1480
150	1510	1389	1642	460	1358	1249	1477
160	1501	1380	1632	470	1355	1246	1474
170	1492	1372	1623	480	1353	1244	1471
180	1484	1365	1614	490	1350	1241	1468
190	1477	1358	1606	500	1347	1239	1465
200	1470	1351	1598	510	1345	1237	1463
210	1463	1345	1591	520	1342	1234	1460
220	1456	1339	1584	530	1340	1232	1457
230	1450	1334	1577	540	1338	1230	1455
240	1444	1328	1571	550	1335	1228	1452
250	1439	1323	1565	560	1333	1226	1450
260	1433	1318	1559	570	1331	1224	1447
270	1428	1313	1553	580	1329	1222	1445
280	1423	1309	1548	590	1326	1220	1443
290	1419	1305	1543	600	1324	1218	1440
300	1414	1300	1538				

Problem 71

WHITE to move and win in three.

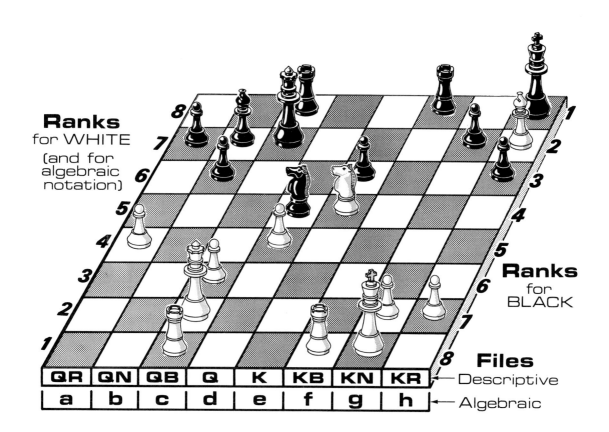

Answer to Problem 71

1. N−KN6 ch	**K** x **B**	1. Ne5-g6 +	**K**h8xh7
2. N x **R** dbl ch	**K−R1** (or **N1**)	2. Ng6xf8 ++	**K**h7-(h8 or g8)
3. Q−KR7 mate		3. Qc2-h7 mate	

This was a situation from an actual game. Only two of the tested players (ratings: 1400 and 1556) missed it.

Problem 72

WHITE to move and win in three.
Here is a golden opportunity that was overlooked by a
chessmaster.

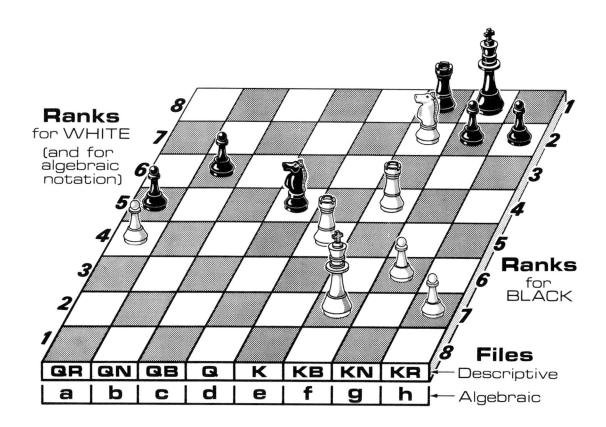

Ranks
for WHITE
(and for
algebraic
notation)

Ranks
for
BLACK

Files

QR	QN	QB	Q	K	KB	KN	KR	— Descriptive
a	b	c	d	e	f	g	h	— Algebraic

Answer to Problem 72

1.N−R6 ch	**P** x N	1. Nf7-h6 +	g7xh6
2.R−KN4 ch	**K−R1**	2. Re4-g4 +	**K**g8-h8
3.R x **R** mate		3. Rf5xf8 mate	

Warm-Up Problem 73

BLACK to move and win in three.

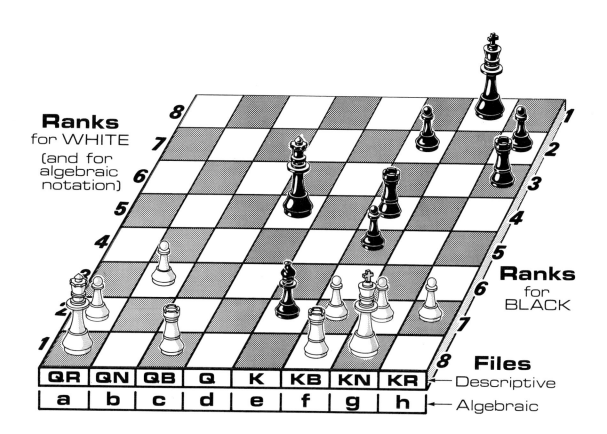

Ranks
for WHITE
(and for
algebraic
notation)

Ranks
for
BLACK

QR	QN	QB	Q	K	KB	KN	KR
a	b	c	d	e	f	g	h

Files ← Descriptive

← Algebraic

177

Answer to Problem 73

1. . . .	Q x P ch	1. . . .	Qd5xg2 +
2. K x Q	R—KN4 ch	2. Kg1xg2	Rf5-g5 +
3. K—R1	B—KB6 mate	3. Kg2-h1	Be2-f3 mate

Every move by BLACK had to be a check of the White King or else WHITE would have had the opportunity to move R—QB8 ch,* which would then be the beginning of the end for BLACK.

*Rc1-c8 +

Alternative Answer

1. . . .	Q x P ch	1. . . .	Qd5xg2 +
2. K x Q	R-KN3 ch	2. Kg1xg2	Rh6-g6 +
3. K-R1 (or K-R3)	B-KB6 (or R-KR4) mate	3. Kg2-h1 (or Kg2-h3)	Be2-f3 (or Rf5-h5) ma

Warm-Up Problem 74

Insert a sheet of paper behind this page to conceal Mate-Rater Problem 75.

WHITE to move and win in three.

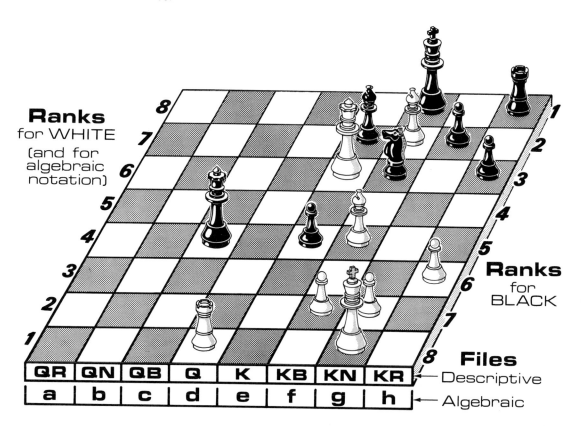

179

Answer to Problem 74

1. R — Q8 ch	**B x R**	1. Rd1-d8 +	**B**e7xd8
2. B — Q6 ch	**B — K2**	2. Bf4-d6 +	**B**d8-e7
3. Q x **B** mate		3. Q6xe7 mate	
or		*or*	
3. B x **B** mate		3. Bd6xe7 mate	

Only two of the tested players, ratings 1286 and 1682, missed this one.

Mate-Rater Problem 75

WHITE to move and win in three.

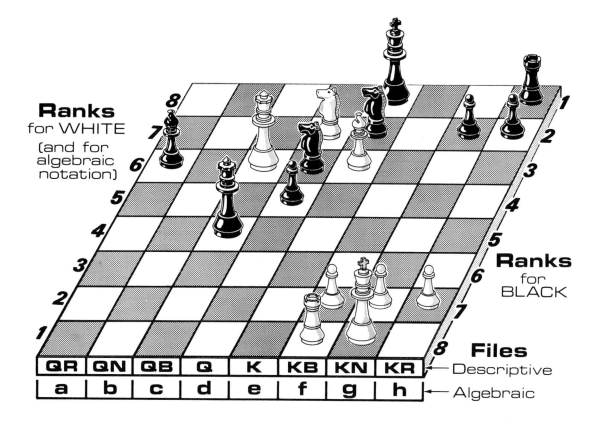

181

Answer to Problem 75

1.N−KB6 dbl ch	**K−B1**
2.Q−K8 ch	**N x Q**
3.N−Q7 mate	

One out of seven tested players missed this. Their ratings ranged from 1180 up to 1682. If you solved it correctly in less than 10 minutes, check your approximate USCF rating on the following table:

1. Nd7-f6 ++	**K**e8-f8
2. Qc6-e8 +	**N**d6xe8
3. Nf6-d7 mate	

Table for Mate-Rater 75

time (sec)	rating	low	high	time (sec)	rating	low	high
5	1993	1858	2138	310	1478	1378	1586
10	1895	1767	2034	320	1475	1375	1583
20	1803	1680	1934	330	1472	1372	1579
30	1751	1632	1878	340	1469	1369	1576
40	1715	1598	1840	350	1465	1366	1572
50	1687	1572	1810	360	1463	1363	1569
60	1665	1552	1786	370	1460	1360	1566
70	1647	1535	1767	380	1457	1358	1563
80	1631	1520	1750	390	1454	1355	1560
90	1617	1507	1735	400	1451	1353	1557
100	1605	1496	1722	410	1449	1350	1554
110	1594	1485	1710	420	1446	1348	1552
120	1584	1476	1699	430	1444	1346	1549
130	1574	1467	1689	440	1441	1343	1547
140	1566	1460	1680	450	1439	1341	1544
150	1558	1452	1672	460	1437	1339	1542
160	1551	1446	1664	470	1435	1337	1539
170	1544	1439	1657	480	1432	1335	1537
180	1538	1433	1650	490	1430	1333	1535
190	1532	1428	1643	500	1428	1331	1532
200	1526	1422	1637	510	1426	1329	1530
210	1521	1417	1632	520	1424	1327	1528
220	1516	1413	1626	530	1422	1325	1526
230	1511	1408	1621	540	1420	1324	1524
240	1506	1404	1616	550	1418	1322	1522
250	1502	1400	1611	560	1416	1320	1520
260	1497	1396	1607	570	1415	1319	1518
270	1493	1392	1602	580	1413	1317	1516
280	1489	1388	1598	590	1411	1315	1514
290	1486	1385	1594	600	1409	1314	1512
300	1482	1381	1590				

Problem 76

WHITE to move and win in three.

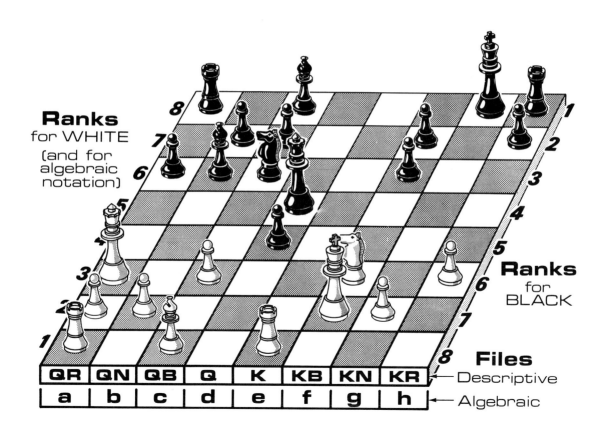

1.Q−KB8 ch	**K** x Q	1. Qa3-f8 +	**K**g8xf8
2.B−KR6 ch	**K−N1**	2. Bc1-h6 +	**K**f8-g8
3.R−K8 mate		3. Re1-e8 mate	

Problem 77

WHITE to move and win in three.

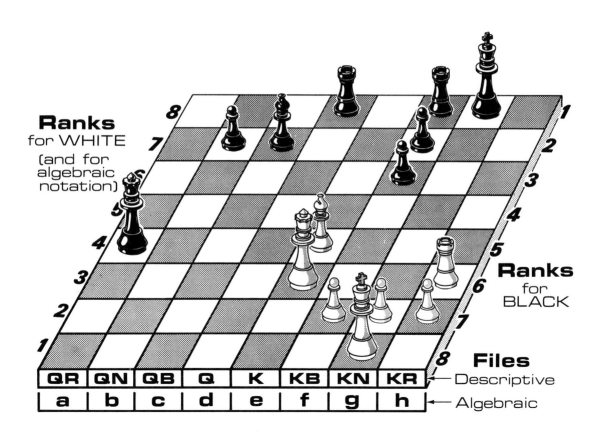

Files								
QR	**QN**	**QB**	**Q**	**K**	**KB**	**KN**	**KR**	← Descriptive
a	**b**	**c**	**d**	**e**	**f**	**g**	**h**	← Algebraic

Ranks
for WHITE
(and for
algebraic
notation)

Ranks
for
BLACK

185

Answer to Problem 77

1.R−KR8 ch	**K x R**	1. Rh3-h8 +	**K**g8xh8
2.Q−KR6 ch	**K−N1**	2. Qe3-h6 +	**K**h8-g8
3.Q−KR7 mate		3. Qh6-h7 mate	

Warm-Up Problem 78

WHITE to move and win in two or three.

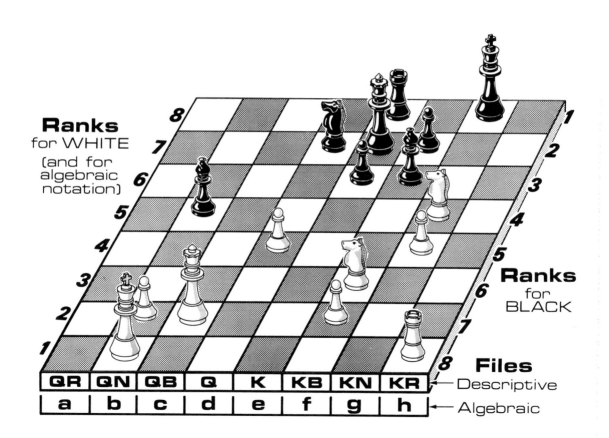

Answer to Problem 78

1.R−KR8 ch	**B** x R	1. Rh1-h8 +	**B**f6xh8
2.Q−KR7 ch	**K−B1**	2. Qc2-h7 +	**K**g8-t8
3.Q x **B** mate		3. Qh7xh8 mate	

or

1.R−KR8 ch	**K** x R	1. Rh1-h8 +	**K**g8xh8
2.Q−KR7 mate		2. Qc2-h7 mate	

Of the 43 rated players only two, ratings: 1180 and 1569, missed this problem.

Warm-Up Problem 79

Insert a sheet of paper behind this page to cover Mate-Rater Problem 80.

WHITE to move and win in three.

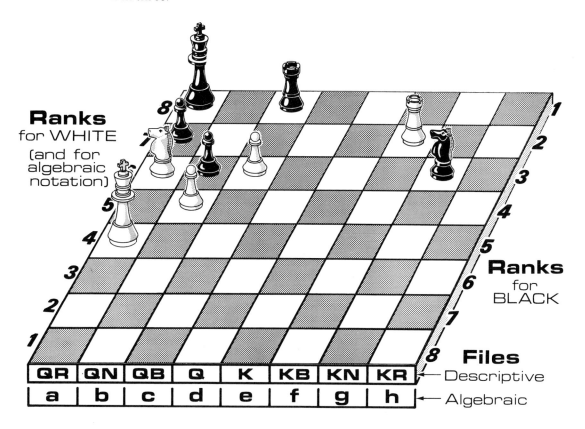

Answer to Problem 79

1.R—QN7

No move by BLACK can now escape mate. The Black Rook must remain on the first rank to protect his King's flank.

Therefore

1. . . . .   **N—K4**

is as good as any, whereupon

2.R—QN8 ch   **R x R**

The Black King is now gasping for air as WHITE moves

3.N—QB 7 mate

This problem stumped one-third of all the tested players. Ratings of those stumped ranged from 1180 to 1938. One player rated 1825 wrote that he was unable to solve it in 20 minutes.

1. Rf7-b7

1. . . .   Ng6-e5

2. Rb7-b8 +   **R**c8xb8

3. Na6-c7 mate

Mate-Rater Problem 80

WHITE to move and win in three.

1. _____ _____
2. _____ _____
3. _____ mate   Time required:

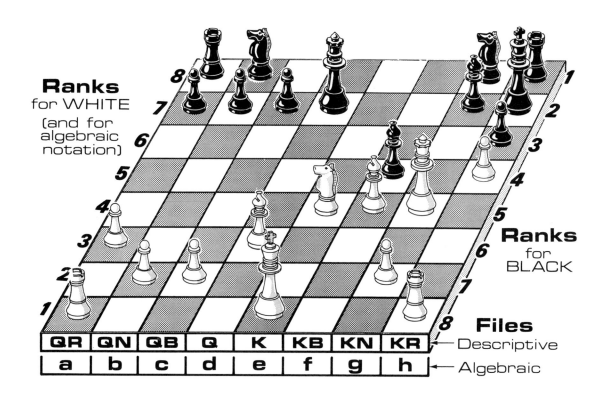

Answer to Problem 80

This is a situation from an actual game with an amateur playing BLACK (note his failure to develop his Knights). BLACK's King is tightly hemmed in and the chessmaster playing WHITE took advantage of this as follows:

1. Q−KN6 ch	**B** x Q
2. N−KN5 ch	**P** x N
3. P x **B** mate	

Around 37% of the players tested were unable to solve this in ten minutes. If you arrived at a correct solution within 10 minutes, the approximate USCF rating at which you performed can be determined from the following table.

1. Qg4-g6 +	**B**f5xg6
2. Ne4-g5 +	h6xg5
3. h5xg6 mate	

Table for Mate-Rater 80

time (sec)	rating	low	high	time (sec)	rating	low	high
5	2220	2027	2431	310	1544	1410	1691
10	2089	1907	2287	320	1540	1406	1686
20	1965	1794	2152	330	1536	1402	1682
30	1896	1732	2077	340	1532	1398	1677
40	1849	1688	2025	350	1528	1395	1673
50	1813	1655	1985	360	1524	1391	1669
60	1784	1629	1954	370	1520	1388	1665
70	1760	1607	1927	380	1517	1385	1661
80	1739	1588	1905	390	1513	1382	1657
90	1722	1572	1885	400	1510	1379	1653
100	1706	1557	1868	410	1507	1376	1650
110	1691	1544	1852	420	1503	1373	1646
120	1679	1533	1838	430	1500	1370	1643
130	1667	1522	1825	440	1497	1367	1640
140	1656	1512	1813	450	1494	1364	1636
150	1646	1503	1802	460	1491	1362	1633
160	1637	1494	1792	470	1489	1359	1630
170	1628	1486	1783	480	1486	1357	1627
180	1620	1479	1774	490	1483	1354	1624
190	1612	1472	1765	500	1480	1352	1621
200	1605	1465	1757	510	1478	1349	1619
210	1598	1459	1750	520	1475	1347	1616
220	1591	1453	1743	530	1473	1345	1613
230	1585	1447	1736	540	1470	1343	1610
240	1579	1442	1729	550	1468	1341	1608
250	1574	1437	1723	560	1466	1338	1605
260	1568	1432	1717	570	1463	1336	1603
270	1563	1427	1712	580	1461	1334	1600
280	1558	1423	1706	590	1459	1332	1598
290	1553	1418	1701	600	1457	1330	1596
300	1549	1414	1696				

Problem 81

WHITE to move and win in three.

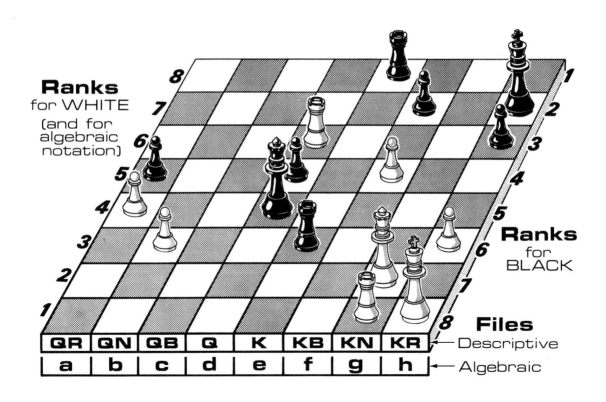

Ranks for WHITE (and for algebraic notation)								**Ranks** for BLACK

QR	QN	QB	Q	K	KB	KN	KR	← Descriptive
a	b	c	d	e	f	g	h	← Algebraic

Files

Answer to Problem 81

1.R x P ch	**K x R**	1. Rd6xh6 +	**K**h7xh6
2.Q—N5 ch	**K—R2**	2. Qg2-g5 +	**K**h6-h7
3.Q—R5 mate		3. Qg5-h5 mate	

Problem 82

WHITE to move and win in three.

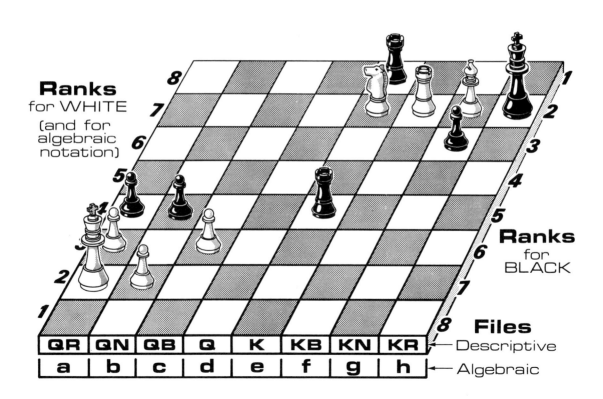

1.B—B8 ch	**K—R1**	1. Bg7-f8 +	**K**h7-h8
2.N x **P** ch	**K—N1**	2. Ne7xg6 +	**K**h8-g8
3.R—N7 mate		3. Rf7-g7 mate	

Warm-Up Problem 83

WHITE to move and win in three.

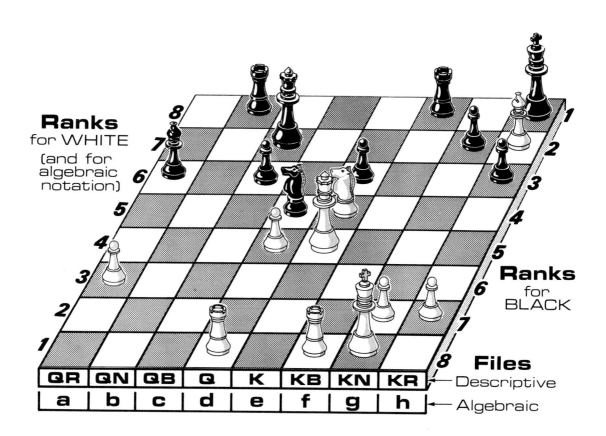

Ranks
for WHITE
(and for
algebraic
notation)

Ranks
for
BLACK

Files

QR	QN	QB	Q	K	KB	KN	KR	— Descriptive
a	b	c	d	e	f	g	h	— Algebraic

Answer to Problem 83

1.N−N6 ch	**K** x B
2.N x **R** dbl ch	**K−N1**
3.Q−R7 mate	

1. Ne5-g6 +	**K**h8xh7
2. Ng6xf8 ++	**K**h7-(h8 or g8)
3. Qe4-h7 mate	

This is essentially a repeat of Problem 71. Almost all the rated players tested appear to have profited from their earlier experience with Problem 71 because nobody missed this. Two players who had failed to solve Problem 71 were now able to solve this.

Warm-Up Problem 84

Place a sheet of paper behind this page to conceal Mate-Rater
Problem 85.

WHITE to move and win in three.

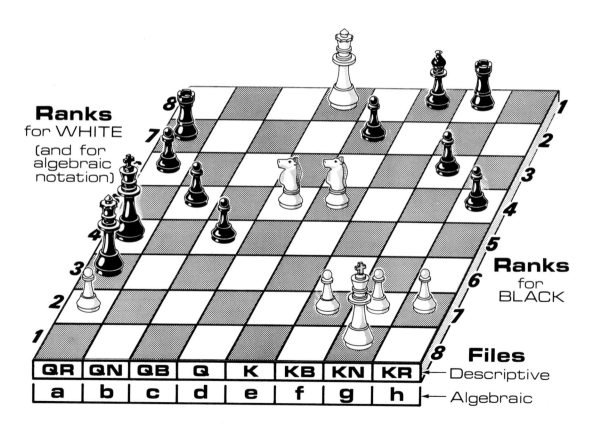

1.Q—R5 ch	**K x Q**	1. Qd8-a5 +	**K**a4xa5
2.N—B6 ch	**K—R5**	2. Ne5-c6 +	**K**a5-a4
3.N—N6 mate		3. Nd5-b6 mate	

Mate-Rater Problem 85

WHITE to move and win in three.

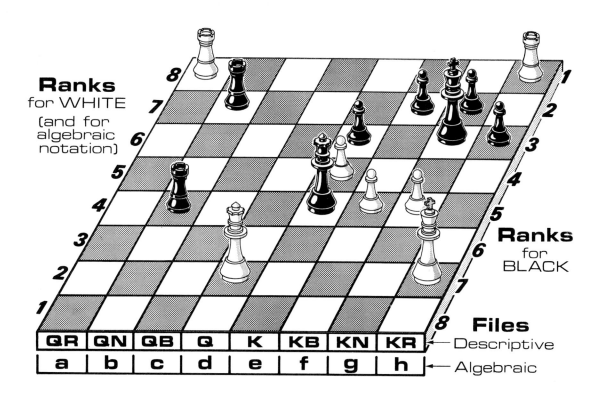

Ranks
for WHITE
(and for
algebraic
notation)

Ranks
for
BLACK

Files

| QR | QN | QB | Q | K | KB | KN | KR | ← Descriptive |
| a | b | c | d | e | f | g | h | ← Algebraic |

Answer to Problem 85

WHITE won a high level tournament game because he recognized that he could force mate in three as follows:

1. P—B5 ch	**P x P**
2. Q x **RP** ch	**P x Q**
3. R(QR8)—KN8 mate	

Almost half of the tested players missed this. The USCF ratings of those who missed ranged as high as 1976. If your solution was correctly arrived at in 10 minutes, the approximate USCF rating at which you performed can be determined from the following table.

1. f4-f5 +	e6xf5
2. Qd2xh6 +	g7xh6
3. Ra8-g8 mate	

Table for Mate-Rater 85

time (sec)	rating	low	high	time (sec)	rating	low	high
5	2281	2100	2477	310	1581	1456	1717
10	2145	1975	2329	320	1577	1452	1712
20	2017	1857	2190	330	1572	1448	1707
30	1945	1791	2112	340	1568	1444	1703
40	1896	1746	2059	350	1564	1440	1699
50	1859	1712	2019	360	1560	1437	1694
60	1829	1685	1986	370	1556	1433	1690
70	1804	1662	1959	380	1553	1430	1686
80	1783	1642	1936	390	1549	1427	1682
90	1765	1625	1916	400	1546	1423	1679
100	1748	1610	1898	410	1542	1420	1675
110	1733	1596	1882	420	1539	1417	1671
120	1720	1584	1868	430	1536	1414	1668
130	1708	1573	1855	440	1533	1411	1664
140	1697	1562	1842	450	1530	1409	1661
150	1686	1553	1831	460	1527	1406	1658
160	1677	1544	1821	470	1524	1403	1655
170	1668	1536	1811	480	1521	1401	1652
180	1659	1528	1802	490	1518	1398	1649
190	1651	1521	1793	500	1515	1395	1646
200	1644	1514	1785	510	1513	1393	1643
210	1637	1507	1777	520	1510	1391	1640
220	1630	1501	1770	530	1508	1388	1637
230	1623	1495	1763	540	1505	1386	1634
240	1617	1489	1756	550	1503	1384	1632
250	1612	1484	1750	560	1500	1382	1629
260	1606	1479	1744	570	1498	1379	1627
270	1601	1474	1738	580	1495	1377	1624
280	1595	1469	1733	590	1493	1375	1622
290	1590	1465	1727	600	1491	1373	1619
300	1586	1460	1722				

Appendix

Statistical Basis for the Mate-Rater Tables

The 42 problems tentatively selected as mate-rater problems were tested on 43 players with current USCF ratings. For each problem the player recorded his solution and the time required to solve the problem. If no solution was found within 10 minutes, the player was instructed to record his time as 10 minutes and to pass on to the next problem. Similarly, if the solution was found to be incorrect, a time of 10 minutes was substituted for the time the player had actually recorded. This imparted a bias to the results but, short of asking the tested players to spend unlimited time until they obtained solutions for all problems, it seemed unavoidable.

The data for each problem were then analyzed statistically. For example, the following types of equations were successively fit by the method of least squares to the data for Mate-Rater 35:

$$R_c = a + bt \qquad \text{(eq. 1)}$$

$$R_c = a + bt + ct^2 \qquad \text{(eq. 2)}$$

$$R_{calc} = at^b \qquad \text{(eq. 3)}$$

$$R_c = ae^{bt} \qquad \text{(eq. 4)}$$

$$R_c = ab^t \qquad \text{(eq. 5)}$$

In the foregoing equations, R_c or R_{calc} indicates the calculated USCF rating, t indicates time required to solve the problem, whereas a, b and c are constants whose values were determined by the regression analyses. The symbol e represents the base of natural logarithms, that is, 2.7182818.... For the five equations, the statistical analysis indicated a negative value for the parameter b as well as for the coefficient of correlation between R and t. In other words, players with higher USCF ratings were likely to require less time to solve Mate-Rater 35. Substituting for a, b and c their least square estimates as obtained by statistical analyses of the data for Mate-Rater 35, Equations 1 to 5 become:

$$R_c = 1793 - 0.983t \qquad \text{(eq. 1)}$$

$$R_c = 1881 - 2.05t + 0.00177t^2 \qquad \text{(eq. 2)}$$

$$R_{calc} = 2899t^{-.1238} \qquad \text{(eq. 3)}$$

$$R_c = 1797\,e^{-.00064t} \qquad \text{(eq. 4)}$$

$$R_c = 1796\,(0.9994)^t \qquad \text{(eq. 5)}$$

The correlation coefficient for equation 3 (-0.79) was little better than for equation 4 (-0.78) or for equations 1 and 5 (-0.76 for each). However, if t is set equal to zero in each of the five equations, the calculated USCF rating is 1793 (eq. 1), 1881 (eq. 2), infinity (eq. 3), 1797 (eq. 4), and 1796 (eq. 5). Thus equation 3 yields the more believable results because only a being of infinite intelligence (and thus capable of an infinite USCF rating) could solve Mate-Rater 35 in zero seconds! Hence only equations of the type indicated by equation 3 were fit to the data for the various mate-raters.

When this was done for the 42 problems originally tested, only 14 yielded correlation coefficients more significant than -0.70. These problems then became the 14 Mate-Raters. They provided a meaningful (inverse) relationship between a player's rating and his time for solving the problem. For these 14 problems, which then became the Mate-Raters, the data best fit an equation of the form

$$R_{calc} = at^b \qquad \text{(eq. 3)}$$

where t is the time required for correct solution and a and b represent constants whose specific values were determined for each Mate-Rater by a standard least-squares analysis of the data. The constant b was always negative in value, as demanded by an inverse relationship between time and rating.

The actual equations used to calculate R_{calc}, the USCF "rating" of the tables, for correct performances in t seconds, were:

Mate-Rater 20, $\qquad R_{calc} = 2280t^{-0.0871}$

Mate-Rater 25, $\qquad R_{calc} = 2522t^{-0.1034}$

Mate-Rater 30, $\qquad R_{calc} = 2594t^{-0.1035}$

Mate-Rater 35, $\qquad R_{calc} = 2899t^{-0.1238}$

Mate-Rater 40, $\qquad R_{calc} = 2511t^{-0.0983}$

Mate-Rater 45, $\qquad R_{calc} = 2464t^{-0.0907}$

Mate-Rater 50, $\qquad R_{calc} = 2747t^{-0.1100}$

Mate-Rater 55, $\qquad R_{calc} = 2488t^{-0.0889}$

Mate-Rater 62, $\qquad R_{calc} = 3400t^{-0.1610}$

Mate-Rater 65, $\qquad R_{calc} = 2190t^{-0.0773}$

Mate-Rater 70, $\qquad R_{calc} = 2427t^{-0.0946}$

Mate-Rater 75, $\qquad R_{calc} = 2240t^{-0.0723}$

Mate-Rater 80, $\qquad R_{calc} = 2559t^{-0.0879}$

Mate-Rater 85, $\qquad R_{calc} = 2632t^{-0.0887}$

The computer program also computed the standard error of estimate of R_{calc} for each Mate-Rater. This permitted the calculation of R_L and R_H, the low and the high values between which the reader's true USCF rating would likely fall in about two-thirds of the cases.